C000164943

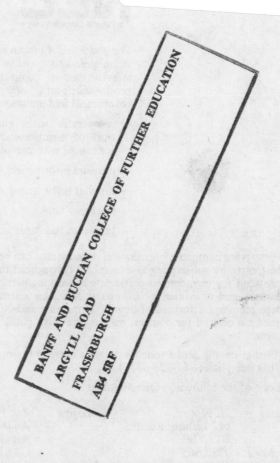

BANFF AND BUCHAN COLLEGE OF FURTHER EDUCATION
ARGYLL ROAD
FRASERBURGH
AB4 5RF

**NCC**
The National Computing Centre

The National Computing Centre develops techniques and provides aids for the more effective use of computers. NCC is a non-profit-distributing organisation backed by government and industry. The Centre

- co-operates with, and co-ordinates the work of, members and other organisations concerned with computers and their use

- provides information, advice and training

- supplies software packages

- publishes books

- promotes standards and codes of practice

Any interested company, organisation or individual can benefit from the work of the Centre by subscribing as a member. Throughout the country, facilities are provided for members to participate in working parties, study groups and discussions, and to influence NCC policy. A regular journal — 'NCC Interface' — keeps members informed of new developments and NCC activites. Special facilities are offered for courses, training material, publications and software packages.

For further details get in touch with the Centre at Oxford Road, Manchester M1 7ED (telephone 061-228 6333)

or at one of the following regional offices

| | | | |
|---|---|---|---|
| Belfast | 1st Floor<br>117 Lisburn Road<br>BT9 7BP | Glasgow | 2nd Floor,<br>Anderston House<br>Argyle Street |
| Telephone: | 0232 665997 | | G2 8LR |
| | | Telephone: | 041-204 1101 |
| Birmingham | 2nd Floor<br>Prudential Buildings<br>Colmore Row<br>B3 2PL | London | 11 New Fetter Lane<br>EC4A 1PU |
| | | Telephone: | 01-353 4875 |
| Telephone: | 021-236 6283 | | |
| Bristol | 6th Floor<br>Royal Exchange Building<br>41 Corn Street<br>BS1 1HG | | |
| Telephone: | 0272 27077 | | |

# Introducing
# the
# Electronic Office

## S. G. Price

PUBLISHED BY THE NATIONAL COMPUTING CENTRE LTD

Keywords for information retrieval (drawn from
*NCC Thesaurus of Computing Terms):* word processing,
data transmission, data collection, office equipment and
activities, personnel management.

British Library Cataloguing in Publication Data

Price, S G
    Introducing the electronic office.
    1.   Electronic office machines
    I.   Title
    651'.2          HF5548

    ISBN 0-85012-204-X

© THE NATIONAL COMPUTING CENTRE LIMITED, 1979

All rights reserved. No part of this publication may be
reproduced, stored in a retrieval system, or transmitted,
in any form or by any means, without the prior
permission of The National Computing Centre.

Published in 1979 by:
NCC Publications, The National Computing Centre Limited,
Oxford Road, Manchester M1 7ED

1st reprint 1980
2nd reprint 1983
Printed in England by H Charlesworth & Co Ltd, Huddersfield

ISBN 0-85012-204-X

# Foreword

by

**Clive Jenkins**
**General Secretary, ASTMS**
**Author (with Barrie Sherman, Director**
**of Research, ASTMS) of**
*The Collapse of Work* **(Eyre Methuen, 1979)**
*White Collar Unionism: The Rebellious Salariat*
**(Routledge and Kegan Paul, 1979)**

Many factors are operating together to influence the patterns of employment in the Western industrialised countries. Some of them are short-term matters, such as the conditions of world trade, the energy crisis and the political policies of individual nations, whilst others, for example the new super competitors and the rapid and increasing pace of technological development, are structural. In technology there is increasing focus on microelectronics: the microprocessor, for example, is widely dubbed 'all-pervasive', 'ubiquitous' and 'revolutionary' in its impact on factory and office alike.

There is endless speculation on the likely effects of microelectronics in the future. Though no-one seems to doubt that the effects will be profound, there is debate as to what form these will take. What will the consequences be for society? In particular, how will employment be affected? Will the new technology generate a vast range of new jobs in fabrication and design? Or will technology-caused unemployment rise drastically in circumstances of social dislocation and political apathy? And what should the attitudes of government, management and trades unions be in this rapidly changing environment?

We have already seen the impact of microelectronics on many industry sectors. It is not alarmist to emphasise what has already happened in order to learn for the future. As one example of the industrial impact of microelectronics — the Swiss watch industry has been shattered by the manufacture of digital watches, mainly in the US: seventeen Swiss firms have collapsed, resulting in widespread unemployment. A similar slump, for similar reasons, has occurred in the West German clock industry.

The replacement of mechanical moving parts by microelectronic devices in cash registers, telephone switching systems and other equipment has affected the employment situation in many areas. In one 5-year period, National Cash Register reduced its manufacturing workforce from 37,000 to 18,000 and over a similar period, American Telephone and Telegraph made workforce cuts from 39,000 to 19,000. Employment in the banking sector has reduced because of computerisation despite a large increase in the volume of business, and there are fears about the likely impact of microprocessor-based word processors in the office environment.

The significance of the microelectronics impact has been acknowledged by government, official bodies and other organisations. Thus in a recent report (The Applications of Semiconductor Technology, September 1978), the Advisory Council for Applied Research and Development declared:

'This is the most influential technology of the twentieth century because: (i) it both extends and displaces a wide range of intellectual or intuitive skills; (ii) it is all-pervasive; (iii) it is still advancing rapidly; (iv) it is very cheap and getting cheaper; (v) it will become abundantly available from international sources and (vi) it has exceptional reliability.'

Similar observations are commonplace in a wide range of technical and general literature.

At the 1978 Trades Union Congress in Brighton, many speakers showed their concern at the social and industrial impact of microelectronics. In his Presidential Address, David Basnett said: 'This new technology will mean a loss of jobs at least as massive as the first technological revolution meant ...... by 1985 in the EEC there will be a net nine million more entrants on the labour market seeking jobs. At the same time a combination of technology and the world economic recession will be destroying jobs faster than they are created.'

The trades union movement has long been interested in the effects of computer technology on society and industry. During the 1956 Trades Union Congress it was declared that 'the effect of mechanisation on clerical employees might be greater than on manual workers'. In 1963 the TUC carried out surveys into the effects of computerisation on office staff, and repeated the survey in 1969. The 1970 annual report observed that 'the introduction of the computer did not appear to have resulted in any overall decrease in staff. The employment issue came to the fore with subsequent developments in the technology of microelectronics.

In September 1978 the TUC debated a motion that focussed specifically on microelectronics. The new technology was seen as posing 'both a challenge and a threat to members'. At the same time it was clear that Luddite pressures were being resisted. The trades unions were suggesting more government support for microelectronics research and application, at the same time looking for ways of protecting members' interests in terms of job security, job status, working conditions and other considerations. It has been emphasised repeatedly that the new technology can benefit people in society, provided that changes to patterns of work are planned in a humane and rational way.

A key area of microelectronics innovation is the office — the subject of the present book. There is increasing talk of the 'automated office' or the 'electronic office', and already such concepts are posing challenges to many traditional practices.

High salary bills and various other factors have encouraged office automation. In one estimate, well over a quarter of a million word-processing stations are now in operation in the US, with two or three operators doing as much work as ten typists and to a higher standard. Such developments have inevitably produced reductions in staffing levels.

It is important to realise that the word processor is only one of the many possible components in the electronic office. A wide range of other devices and concepts are profiled in this book. Individually and together, they challenge existing work patterns, forcing a careful re-examination of office operating philosophies and business policies. It is essential, for example, to consider how the office can be helped to develop its crucial support role for management and professional staff.

We should also emphasise that the character of automation — how it is introduced, how it works, the impact on employees — is up to us. Technological innovation has a natural momentum but it is human beings who take the decisions. We can decide the policies and priorities, with the objectives of making office work easier and more efficient, more able to perform its supportive and other tasks, without at the same time threatening the job satisfaction of staff or their employment security. As the only way that such objectives can be met is by consent, the role of management and unions negotiating — within Technology Agreement frameworks with the government creating the right environment — is of critical importance.

In making a useful contribution to the current debate, the present book performs a two-fold task: it acquaints readers with the components and shape of the electronic office; and at the same time it gives due weight to the fact that offices and organisations are about people as well as equipment.

I welcome this publication and hope it will help to stimulate discussion, not only about the impact of microelectronics in the office environment, but also about the continuous technology-caused change that is inevitable in our society and what responses have to be made.

# Acknowledgements

This book is a distillation of other people's experiences and opinions. A wide range of users, suppliers, government agencies and research organisations have contributed to its contents. The author wishes to thank the following people who passed technical comment on the first draft:

G. B. Bleazard    NCC Limited
K. Edwards        ICI Limited
N. West           P.O. Telecommunications H.Q.
A. Paterson       Logica VTS Limited

Thanks are also due to the following people and organisations for their time and their ideas:

Association of Professional, Executive, Clerical and Computer Staff (APEX), London
Augmentation Resources Centre, Tymshare Inc. California
Bank of America, California
Barclays Bank International Limited, Poole
British Olivetti Limited, London
Burmah Engineering Company Limited, Manchester
Richard Canning, Canning Publications Inc. California
Central Computer Agency, London
CIBA-Geigy (UK) Ltd, Manchester
Clydesdale Bank Ltd, Glasgow
Dun & Bradstreet International Ltd., New York
IBM Word Processing Systems Support Centre, Dallas
IBM United Kingdom Limited
ICI Ltd, Central Management Services
ICI (Pharmaceuticals) Limited
International Computers Limited
Logica VTS Limited, London
National Bank Examiners, Controller of Currency, Dallas
National Economic Development Office, London

National Water Council, London
Jack M Nilles, Office of Interdisciplinary Programs,
    University of Southern California
Plessey Office Systems Ltd, Nottingham
Post Office, Martlesham
Rank Xerox (UK) Limited, London
Systime Limited, Leeds
Telecom Australia, Melbourne
Work Research Unit, Department of Employment, London
Xerox Corporation, California
Young & Rubicam New York, New York

The Centre acknowledges with thanks the support provided by the Computer, Systems and Electronics Requirement Board (CSERB) for the project from which this publication derives.

# Preface

The electronic office as a *total integrated information system* is very much a concept of the future, but evolution towards it is clearly evident today. This book deals with current developments.

A look is taken at the environment of office automation, how this is affecting individuals and organisations. Current attitudes and their impact on the realisation of the benefits of office automation are considered. Available products and services suitable for the electronic office are profiled. Finally suggestions are made as to what an organisation must do today to exploit the electronic office of tomorrow.

This book is a scene-setter, exploring possibilities, benefits and problems, and outlining the products available today. It is the intention that future work of a more in-depth nature will look at the design, implementation and operation of the electronic office.

# PREFATORY NOTE

Since the first printing of this book, there have been a number of developments in the field of office automation. Many of the emerging technologies originally discussed have now yielded commercial products, and there have been changes to the environment within which the services are provided:

— The British Telecom Act and the liberalisation programme may be expected to produce major climatic changes in the supply of telecommunication services in the next decade. These changes are already evident in the licences being granted to non-BT organisations to offer public electronic mail services.

— A Teletex text-communication service is operational in Sweden and West Germany, and the UK, in common with many other nations, is embarking upon a Teletex trial.

— British Telecom has now published a national directory of facsimile numbers. Users of the directory will be able to look up the numbers of other companies and to establish whether the machines are compatible.

— Optical disk systems now offer economic high-volume, fast-access storage of both image and character string information. This technology should be considered for all archival and reference data applications.

— Office systems using local area networks are now installed in the UK. Some are networks of purpose-built devices, whilst others utilise off-the-shelf microcomputers.

— With several recent announcements, the office system using a Private Automatic Branch Exchange (PABX) is now a realistic option and promises to keep user organisations puzzling about the correct 'total solution' for their circumstances.

— Several UK companies now offer office system products, and the Government has established a pilot project scheme to encourage the use of office equipment which has a high

British content. The suppliers currently covered by the scheme include:

> ABS Computers
> Aregon
> Data Recall
> GEC
> IBM(UK)
> ICL
> Office Technology Limited(OTL)
> Plessey Office Systems
> Rank Xerox
> Rediffusion Computers
> Systime
> Xionics

At the conceptual level the book is largely unaffected by the changes; the messages presented and the considerations discussed remain valid. The prices of products in the book are left at the 1979 level. The majority of prices quoted have remained the same or perhaps have dropped slightly.

S G Price
July 1982

# Contents

# 1   Environment and Scope

## INTRODUCTION

The concept of the electronic office is capturing the imagination of many people. It is currently receiving a large amount of business (and general interest) media coverage. The state of technology and its related economics, together with the current environment, are encouraging large and small businesses, unions and individuals, to be interested in the impact, the problems and the potential of office automation.

Major changes in office practice have been effected by various technological developments. For example, electric motors gave rise to the electric typewriter, faster printing machines and collators: documents could be produced more quickly and to a higher standard. The electric motor was also the basis of the early data processing machines, the tabulators and sorters.

The telephone has made the whole world available to those people wishing to engage in convenient person-to-person communication, and has consequently speeded up business transactions and decision-taking. Later magnetic recording facilitated data storage and manipulation facilities on computer devices; and voice storage on dictation and telephone answering machines.

The above factors and others have changed substantially the way that office work is done. The quality and throughput of work has increased and information available to managers is now more accurate and more current. All this enables organisations to work more effectively.

Although the changes wrought were major they were only introduced slowly, and only when the environment and the economics were right. Innovation could only be justified in cost terms: either the new techniques were cheaper or would lead to future cost savings.

1

Today two developments – the microprocessor and tele-communications advances – are creating possibilities for information creation, storage, retrieval and movement that have never existed before. For example, microprocessors in voice recognition units are opening the way for speech input of information; in typewriters and in word processors, microprocessors are providing text-editing facilities. Microprocessor-controlled lasers, together with photocopying technology, are providing image printers which are capable of producing, at a high speed, sheets of intermixed text and graphic information and retaining the convenience-photocopier capability.

Satellites are now offering information transmission speeds of around 7 million bits per second (or the equivalent of the information on 300 typed A4 sheets per second), and developments in optic-fibre communications are promising speeds of 1000 million bits per second (the equivalent of 40,000 typed A4 sheets/second). Such high-speed communications will enhance the value of existing information handling. These advances create opportunities for the development of services which could handle the bulk of current business mail.

The telecommunications authorities worldwide are formulating proposals for an international text communication service, Teletex. It is proposed that this service will be communications network independent. So, unlike Telex, which runs on a dedicated low-grade network, Teletex can always use the networks most appropriate for the volume of traffic, and need never find itself using outdated and inadequate facilities.

Advances in technology alone only create an opportunity for change. For that change to be effected the economics and the environment need to be right. The bulk of the technology needed for the full electronic office is here today. Some of it needs a little refinement and some of the economics are not yet right. Any problems of technology and economics are minor by comparison to the challenges issued by existing social, cultural and organisational attitudes, and those challenges must be faced if the most effective use is to be made of the technology available.

## WHAT IS MOTIVATING PEOPLE?

There have been dramatic changes in the costs of running an office. These include the increasing cost of staff and the decreasing cost of equipment; and the supply position and cost of fuel oil for transport and heating. These economic changes, together with a growing realisation that we are an information-based society, are creating the interest in the application of technology to support all aspects of office activity. These main forces which are motivating people to look at the electronic office are covered in the following sections.

## Rising Cost of Skilled Support Staff

There is an increasing shortage of skilled and experienced support staff. In June 1978 there were 35,994[1] vacancies for clerical and related staff in the UK; of that figure 8,799[1] were for personal secretaries, shorthand typists and typists.

When considering the number of vacancies that must be handled by the typing and secretarial agencies, this official Department of Employment figure is probably very low and it is more likely that an often quoted figure of 25,000 vacancies in London alone is nearer the truth.

In 1979 the secretarial agency Alfred Marks Bureau estimated that in the London area there are 6 jobs for every skilled secretary and typist available, and that about 50% of the people available for work have no significant office experience. Employers who wish to attract experienced staff have to pay competitive salaries, and have to offer very good working conditions. Organisations prepared to train inexperienced staff will find that staff will leave for better jobs after training has been received. In this sort of environment any opportunities to reduce staff requirements will be welcomed.

Not only are clerical staff costing more to employ, they are also forming an increasing proportion of the workforce. In the UK manufacturing industries (ie excluding utilities, government and commerce), 28.4% of workers fall into the administrative clerical and technical classification.[2]

The graph of the breakdown of the total US labour force from 1860 (Figure 1) shows the proportion of people engaged in the information occupations rising dramatically from less than 20% in 1950 to 50% in 1975; the prediction is that it will keep on rising.[3]

[1] Department of Employment, August 1978
[2] Department of Employment, December 1978
[3] Parker and Porat 1975

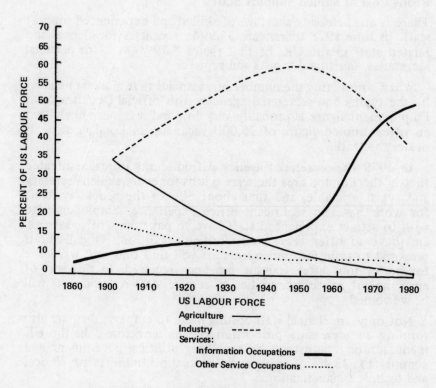

Figure 1  Information Sector of US Labour Force
(Based on Parker and Porat 1975)

This is perhaps a reflection of the comparative investments that have been made on the shop and the office, or perhaps of the increasing importance of information to modern business. Either way the cost of providing the information required and the cost of staffing an office are increasing.

## Cost and Performance of Equipment

Together with the rising cost of labour, the most significant force lowering the threshold in the move towards the electronic office is the decreasing cost of equipment.

The cost of computer processors has tumbled over the past ten years; a 20% per annum decrease in price per unit performance has been experienced. This level of change is expected to continue over the next decade. However, small computer systems, such as would form the basis of word processors, are expected to show an even faster decrease. This will be in the region of 35% per year.[1] These decreases are shown in Figure 2.

It should be noted that these decreases in cost will not be reflected in full in the price of the equipment on the market. Firstly the cost of peripherals is only falling at about 12% per year, and in the small systems these items can form more than half of the total cost. Secondly the manufacturers can be expected to be offering more computer power and more refined systems at a slightly lower price rather than same power for considerably less.

Peripheral storage devices (magnetic disk and tape drives) and printers have a high proportion of mechanical components, and cost reductions have been more difficult to achieve than in computer processors. However, advances in speeds of access to stored data and in the storage device capacities are such that a small system user in 1985 could expect to have immediate access to 100 million characters where today he has access to 1 million.

Bubble memory and holographic optical stores are the technologies likely to replace the disk devices in the next five years and provide those increases in storage capacity. Bubble memory can be expected to offer capacities of $10^{11}$ bits compared to the 2 x $10^9$ bits of magnetic disk with holographic storage offering up to $10^{13}$ bit storage.

[1] SITPRO 1978

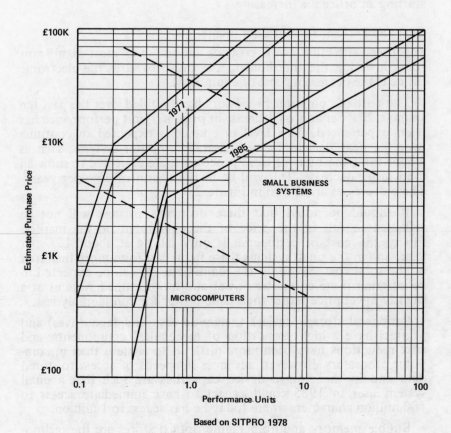

Figure 2   Estimated Cost/Performance of Small Computers
(CPU + Memory Prices only)

For the real significance of these increases to be meaningful in the electronic office environment, advances in data base management also have to be made. The storage and retrieval of bulk unstructured textual information will require the possibility of indexing the information at capture and of this mass storage being content-addressable. The usage of this volume of information by the unsophisticated user will place further demands on the efforts of the data base management systems designers for the provision of increasingly simple interfaces.

The major reason for the cost reductions is the silicon chip microprocessor. The microprocessor is not only providing price/performance cuts but also, because of its small size and inherent reliability, is suitable for use in a far wider range of environments than were earlier computers. Hence computing power can now be introduced into an ordinary office environment without expensive special air-conditioning and power supplies. Terminals can be easily moved; indeed some are designed in briefcase-like carriers and can be used at home or in hotel rooms and can communicate with other computer devices through an ordinary telephone.

It has been estimated that the price of a communicating word processor, which includes magnetic storage and printing capability, will fall by 70% to 80% by 1987.[1] As a result of this, it can be envisaged that it may well be considered the norm for organisations to use such equipment and that the communicating word processor (or whatever) will sit next to the phone in every office.

## Reduction in Quality of Mail Service

It is generally accepted that the quality of postal service has declined over the past decade. Whatever the reason for the decline, be it economies to keep charges down or the large increase in volume of the mail handled, alternative message-delivery systems are being used where urgency is imperative.

The table below shows the costs per single page of sending firstly a single page and secondly 10 pages by various methods.

[1] Pye 1979

| Method | Rate | Delivery | Cost per Page (pence) | |
|---|---|---|---|---|
| | | | Single page | 10 pages |
| 1st class mail | | 1 – 2 day | 9 | 1.25 |
| Telex | | immediate | 57 | 57 |
| Facsimile | | | | |
| 6 minute | peak | " | 108 | 108 |
| | standard | " | 72 | 72 |
| 3 minute | peak | " | 54 | 54 |
| | standard | " | 36 | 36 |
| 1 minute | peak | " | 18 | 18 |
| | standard | " | 12 | 12 |
| Text Comms. | peak | " | 6 | 3.3 |
| | standard | " | 3 | 2.1 |

(The figures are based on P.O. charges current in September 1978, on A4 pages containing 2500 characters, on facsimile and text transmissions being made over the public switched telephone network for a distance greater than 56 kilometers[1].)

Other non-electronic methods of urgent delivery involve in-house messengers or courier services which are expensive but may be the only means of meeting requirements. This is because, excepting Telex, which is not very suitable for bulk information, the other electronic methods can only be used where thoughtful and exclusive arrangements have been made between sender and recipient.

Of these methods in the table only the mail and the telex are at present offered as public services, but the Post Office does intend to introduce a public facsimile service[2] and through CCITT is involved in the definition of the Teletex text communication service.

Following the recent decision of the UK Post Office to separate mail and telecommunications the economics of information distribution services could radically alter, and could affect the rate of introduction of text communication services and the setting of the tariffs for such services.

[1] Pugh 1978
[2] Robinson 1978

## Other Increasing Costs

Although not as significant as rising labour costs, other costs of running office activities are contributing to the interest being shown in office automation. These include the cost of office supplies, such as paper, filing cabinets, and other furniture. The UK wholesale price index for paper and board was 131 for the third quarter of 1978 compared with 100 for 1975.[1] The costs of transporting people to meetings, and the payment of inner-city salary weightings to compensate for costs of travel to work, are escalating.

The supply position and price of fuel oil is increasingly important in transportation and office heating considerations. Cost comparisons of the physical movement of both information and people and the alternative electronic movement of information are increasingly favouring the latter.

The annual rental for modern office space in central Manchester is now in the region of £3.50 per square foot, whilst in London rents can be in the region of £20 per square foot, with rates and service charges capable of matching these figures.

In this environment of rising costs any opportunities to minimise their impact will be welcomed by all organisations.

## Familiarity

Although not necessarily a corporate motivation, familiarity with products and knowledge of the potential for using those products will remove obstacles to the introduction of much electronic equipment into the office environment.

Computer-inspired equipment is increasingly entering the home. It arrives in the form of television games, as personal computers with home application packages, as aids to spelling; it is also present in the form of the calculator. The Post Office is introducing Prestel, an information and message service based on the domestic television set and the telephone.

As individuals gain familiarity with equipment at home and develop trust in its capabilities, they will expect to see the equipment in use in the work environment. And if nothing is provided at work then employees could well bring in their own devices from home. This has happened with the calculator; as costs continue to fall, it will also happen with other equipment.

[1] Business Monitor PQ481, 1978

Familiarity and awareness will be gained through sharing a colleague's experiences and enthusiasm, and will create demands for equipment. Such demands will, as costs fall, be increasingly met through casual expenditure rather than through official purchasing policies. Equipment such as Commodore PETs and APPLE microcomputers are being bought as 'office equipment' rather than as 'computers', even though five years ago the same capability would have cost 50 times the amount.

## Competitive Environment

One motivating force which only has an effect when there is awareness of the possibilities is the need for an organisation to remain competitive. That competitiveness may be judged as quality of output, speed of response to customers' requirements, speed of entry to markets, and accuracy of information enabling markets to be exploited.

A few organisations, conscious of the need to create an advantage over their competitors, are constantly alert for opportunities. These organisations are the innovative ones prepared to pay the cost of being in a position to take those opportunities as they arise. However, most organisations tend to be followers and will take advantage of new opportunities only when other companies have demonstrated the benefits. The followers then need to adopt new techniques to remain competitive.

## Value of Information

There is a growing recognition of the fact that information is a valuable part of the production of goods and the provision of services. People who discuss resources are now starting to talk of land, labour, capital and information. The value of information will be the most powerful long-term force in motivating the development of the electronic office. Currently, quantifying the value of full information delivered quickly and properly cross referenced can only be simply done in a narrow band of commercial environments, eg foreign exchange, commodities dealing, pharmaceuticals research. Consequently the majority of the early implementations of office automation are concerned with word processing and typing enhancement since it is the only part of the electronic office which reduces manpower and demonstrates quantifiable benefits. The other considerations, excepting the competitive element, are of relatively minor importance to the performance and survival of the organisation as a whole.

## OFFICE ACTIVITY

The total information system of an organisation can be divided into two areas: *data processing* and *informal office systems.* Historically, data processing deals with the formal side of company information handling and works to a set of well-defined rules for each application. It presents formal interfaces to its users through forms and procedure manuals and it demands rigorous job training for its operators. Data processing accepts predictable input and produces predictable output. Changes to these systems are introduced by re-definition and re-specification. Much of this output is essential to company operation: eg invoices, payslips, production schedules.

Informal office systems, on the other hand, operate in the more undefined areas of office activity. Typically they attend to tasks which are performed as required in a manner suitable for that moment. They are systems designed by the user for his own particular purpose. Rules are not entirely absent from informal systems. Common-sense and traditional protocols do provide a base for procedures. Familiar examples are business letter layout and telephone answering habits. In some organisations letter house styles have been adopted, thus formalising an informal system. Users of such systems require a general skill training rather than the strict job training of dp systems, and changes to informal systems occur by evolution.

The boundaries between data processing and informal office systems can be hazy and are likely to become more so as more activities are automated. Because the equipment used in automating office systems derived from the computers used in the widespread automation of data processing, it is not surprising that a distinction cannot always be drawn.

The one place where data processing and informal office systems do meet is in the accessing of the company data base. The full force of the strict data processing systems has created a well-defined corporate data base, holding details of the company's operations. This information will then be used quite informally; it will be referred to in meetings as a basis for taking decisions; it will be boasted about in press releases; and it will be mentioned in warnings about poor productivity.

## THE INFORMAL OFFICE

Work in the informal office environment is in four categories:

- *document preparation,* covering dictation, and typing and updating of documents through to duplicating, copying and the use of typesetting services;

- *message distribution,* including telephoning, mail services, and travel for meetings;

- *personal information management,* including the use of local filing cabinets, in/out trays, diaries and planning charts and which can be extended to the filing of information contributing to a corporate data base, eg correspondence registration;

- *information access,* including reference to directories, timetables and catalogues, and the use of library and bibliographic services and access to corporate data bases.

It is to these four categories that electronic office technology can be applied, not only to do existing tasks more efficiently but also to allow new tasks to be performed. This gives not only the ability to provide information more accurately and in a more timely manner but also the ability to provide information that was not usefully available before.

The four areas of office activity are shown below in terms of the conventional constituents of those activities compared with the elements of the electronic office that may be used in the future.

Although the four areas of activity are shown separately there is a great deal of interaction and interdependence. For example, the arrangement and confirmation of a meeting between two people involves all four areas:

1 telephone conversation deciding
  upon need                                    — message distribution

2 access and update of diaries
  to fix a date                                — personal information
                                                 management

3 access of train/flight information
  to fix the time                              — information access

4 preparation of a letter to
  confirm the meeting                          — document preparation

5 despatch of the letter                       — message distribution

6 registration of the letter                   — personal information
                                                 management

## Document Preparation

| Conventional | Electronic Office |
|---|---|
| Shorthand | Dictation |
| Dictation machine | Shorthand keypad |
| Longhand | Character recognition |
| Typing | Voice recognition |
|     cut and paste | Word processing |
|     error correction fluid |     text manipulation |
|     total retype |     text storage |
| Carbon copies |     text retrieval |
| Spirit duplication |     quality printing/Braille printing |
| Photocopy | Intelligent copier |
| Typesetting services | In-house photocomposition |
| | Microfilm systems |

## Message Distribution

| Conventional | Electronic Office |
|---|---|
| Telephone | Telephone — voice store and forward |
| |     sophisticated exchanges |
| Telegram | |
| Telex | Telex and Teletex |
| Courier | Facsimile and hybrid OCR/facsimile |
| Internal mail | Communicating word processors |
| P.O. mail | Prestel message service |
| Meetings | Computer conferencing |
| | Confravision service |
| | Office at home |

## Personal Information Management

| Conventional | Electronic Office |
|---|---|
| Filing cabinets | Electronic filing cabinet |
| Index cards | Document registration |
| Check lists | Indexing and cataloguing aids |
| In/out trays | File sharing |
| Diary | Mass storage |
| Planning boards | |

## Information Access

| Conventional | Electronic Office |
|---|---|
| Written enquiries | eg Viewdata, eg Prestel |
| Telephone enquiries | Information broadcast systems, eg Oracle/Ceefax (teletext) |
| Catalogues/timetables | Touchtone telephone input, voice synthesiser output |
| The media | Access to computerised information bases |
| Procedure manuals | |
| Directories | Company database Microfilm retrieval systems |

## SCOPE AND BENEFITS OF OFFICE AUTOMATION

The benefits of office automation are summarised in the phrase 'contributes to an increased individual and corporate effectiveness'. Such benefits are achieved in two ways; firstly by cost-saving applications, and secondly by added-value applications. Of the two it is added-value applications which gives the full potential of office automation. However, to realise the benefits, the value of information to the organisation has to be recognised.

Cost-saving benefits are aimed at reducing staff costs or equipment costs or increasing work volume throughput without increasing staff. Cost-saving benefits are the justification for the majority of today's word processor implementations, where the objective is the streamlining of typing services.

Added-value applications on the other hand aim at realising four principal benefits:

— increased information accessibility;

— increased people accessibility;

— increased control over personal activities;

— increased individual contribution.

Through these, corporate and individual effectiveness can be improved.

Increased information accessibility can give information which is more current and more accurate and can give an ability to search for and to define requirements of that information quickly and cheaply. Public, closed community, company and personal information can thus be made more readily available, and can be easily updated, thereby giving all users instant access to the latest version.

Increased people accessibility can be realised through the possibility of non-simultaneous contacts. Message systems will permit people to communicate efficiently, even though both of the parties are geographically separated or are not simultaneously available. The percentage of business calls that fail because the required person was not available has been estimated to be as high as 70%. The problems of time zones and conflicting activities can cease to be a barrier to effective communication. Conferencing systems, or file-sharing systems allow geographically separate co-workers to contribute to joint work, to enter discussions and to take joint decisions on a continuing basis without the inconvenience of travel and the problems of arranging mutually convenient meeting times.

Increased control over personal activities is gained through an ability to work from a variety of locations. Using intelligent terminals, all the information required could be available from any desk in an organisation, from home and from hotel rooms. With message systems, individuals will be able to control when they wish to look at messages rather than suffering constant telephone interruption whilst trying to concentrate for a period.

Finally an increased individual contribution is achieved because an individual can spend more time on his primary task rather than an ancillary but necessary support task. Not only can people use access to information and use reliable and fast communications to perform their task better but they can also have more time in which to perform their primary task. For example, not only will a purchasing manager be able to buy the goods currently considered to be the most appropriate at the best price, ensuring the best delivery, but will have more time to consider alternatives and to enter purchasing negotiations.

Added-value applications have far broader implications than does the displacement of some support staff. Opportunities arise for significant increases in organisational effectiveness.

Of office workers in engineering and related industries (May 1977), about 50% were managerial and professional and 40% were supportive clerical[1] which, if considered as proportions of the office wage bill, could probably be 70% managerial and professional and 15% supportive clerical. These figures illustrate the scale of potential benefits that could be realised by supporting the activities of managers and professional workers.

Reliable and fast message delivery, instant recall of personal files, and access to corporate and public information bases, are the types of facilities that could support the manager and the professional worker. These are the people who provide the organisation with the information it needs to be competitive, who take decisions based on (hopefully) accurate and current data.

These are people who spend a large part of their job originating and discussing working drafts of documents and travelling to meetings for discussions. It is these people who can derive the full benefits from office automation. They can be given the support in their activities which allows them to concentrate on their true tasks. This type of support allows a manager to manage better and to manage more; the professional can access and use more of the right information.

That type of benefit, the added-value benefit, is however difficult to quantify. How is the value of a manager's time measured? By number of subordinates? How is that value balanced against the cost of the support equipment? By size of budget? What is the value of information to the organisation? What is the benefit of

[1] Department of Employment, July 1978

getting that information faster?

Here is a problem. Currently, office automation equipment is expensive; investment in the office sector is usually only granted as a result of demonstrable cost savings. But the benefits of supporting the manager and professional are that it allows them to do more. There is the opportunity for adding value to their contribution to the organisation.

## CURRENT ACTIVITY

Of the office automation activities it is the document preparation area that is receiving most of the attention. Personal-information, management-document communication and information access areas are being explored by some innovative organisations, with others showing an interest in any resulting experiences.

Automation of document preparation is the centre of activity for several reasons:

- it is an easy concept to grasp;
- the benefits are measurable;
- the first steps need no large investment;
- automation can be started without the collaboration required of document communication.

Document preparation is an easy concept to grasp. At its simplest it is an enhancement of the typing function, and the automation of existing tasks. Word processing can be related to current activities, with the raw material and the finished product being the same, when dictation or long-hand are used for input to produce the typed page as output. Use of the 'electronic filing cabinet' and enquiring for supplier prices on a terminal require more awareness of the whole area.

The benefits of document preparation are observable and quantifiable. If only the erroneous text needs to be re-keyed typists spend far less time in correcting and revising work and when a predefined letter can be amalgamated with a selection of entries on a name-and-address file to produce 'personal circulars', the typist's involvement is minimal and every recipient will have a quality letter. If contracts are produced using standard paragraphs the checking of drafts is considerably reduced.

These benefits are measurable and can be quantified in terms of staff saving and increased throughput, so that positive cost benefits can be demonstrated. On the other hand the benefits attributable to faster electronic document communication and to better access to information are mostly intangible and are not readily accepted as justification for investment in new equipment, even by the most enlightened management.

Document preparation can yield its principal benefits without the need for any large investment, and without the need for collaboration with other parties. A single stand-alone word processor can be supplied, plugged into the mains and used immediately. The user is in a low-risk situation, with minimum commitment and immediately observable results.

However, document communication cannot be achieved without some thoughtful exclusive relationship being established between two or more parties. With communicating word processors there are no standards commonly in use which would guarantee that two different makes of word processor could pass messages to each other. Even with facsimile, an area in which the telephone authorities have established sets of international standards, intending users still have to make specific arrangements with each other. Such arrangements are usually made on the basis of applying such technology to a specific task within a community of interest, eg newspaper photograph transmission. General message systems will yield little benefit until there are a substantial number of users on such a system, and this will require a high investment to establish, and the high investment will have to be made as the basis of unquantifiable benefits.

The interest in document preparation activities is quite intense with new word processing vendors entering the market every month. 56 UK vendors were listed in a 'Which Computer?' suppliers guide in January 1979, compared with 14 vendors in the Autumn of 1976. The world market is estimated to be in the region of $500 million with an annual production of over 50,000 units. Although the market is growing, a look at the number installed, compared with facsimile units and telex terminals, reveals that the market is in its infancy.

Word processors, which have application in both document preparation and message distribution areas, numbered approximately 350,000 (world-wide) in December 1977 (source: International Data Corporation). Facsimile and telex, used purely for message distribution, numbered 390,000 (source: Institute for Graphic Communications) and 1 million (source P.O.) respectively.

Word processing usage is growing, and communicating word

processors have the potential to replace the bulk of the facsimile and telex placements in addition to remaining the centre of office automation. The time within which that potential can be realised will depend mainly on either the development and application of international standards for text communication, or on the introduction of an international text communication service. The national telephone administrations are currently discussing such a service: 'Teletex'. This service will be the product of international agreement and will specify the minimum characteristics of a terminal wishing to use the service. It is likely that details of 'Teletex' will be agreed long before word-processing manufacturers could agree on communication standards for their equipment. Consequently many manufacturers will find themselves changing their products to conform to 'Teletex' requirements in order to enter that potentially huge market of users who want to combine fast reliable communications with word-processing and other office activities.

# 2 What Will the Electronic Office Look Like?

The electronic office will manifest itself in various ways; its exact nature and facilities will be dictated by the needs of the individual organisation and individual user. The user will see the electronic office as a single work-station, making available to the user all the facilities required.

It would be unreasonable to imagine that facilities would be available through a series of separate work-stations: one for electronic mail, one for Prestel (the Post Office public information service) one for word processing, etc. However, for the next few years until either the full electronic office is available as an off-the-shelf product or as a series of fully compatible products, that is the situation facing users. In terms of today's products, the work-station can be imagined as being similar to a screen-based stand-alone word processor through which the user has access to data-banks, electronic mail systems and other work-stations.

The 'model' electronic office will have five main components:

— work-station;

— local area communications;

— access to central facilities;

— private branch exchange;

— access to external facilities.

These could be related as in Figure 3.

## WORK-STATION COMPONENTS

The work-station may have a keyboard, a visual display screen, local magnetic storage, local processing power, and a quality printer. The high-resolution screen may have graphics facilities for both line art graphics display and for the display of facsimile transmissions and other digitised images. For the printing of

21

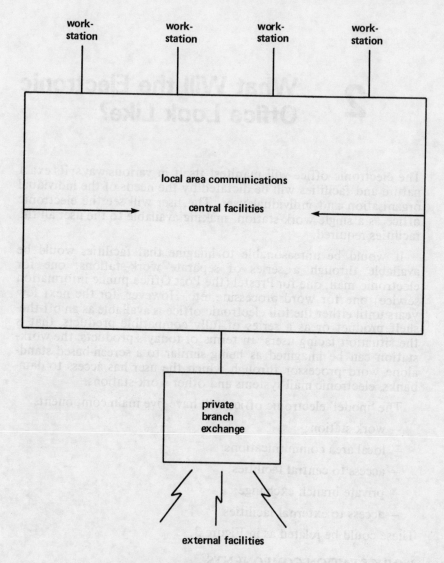

Figure 3   The Electronic Office — Components

graphics a non-impact image printer will be required; in the short term, for economic reasons, this will probably need to be a shared central facility, but in the longer term it may be possible — and desirable — for this to be provided in the work-station. This would then provide multifont character and graphic printing, and provide a convenient copying capability. The Wang Image Printer, which currently sells at $35,000 in the USA, is the type of technology being considered here although at that price it could only be considered for use as a shared facility. The Wang Image Printer uses optic fibre to transfer the image (text or graphics) as generated on a cathode ray tube screen to the photoreceptor of a xerographic print facility which can output paper at 18 A4 sheets/ min. Other developments in this area are of laser-driven printers. It is this technology that Xerox is using in their office automation trials. With this equipment images are described by a program controlled laser again, to be transferred to paper by a standard xerographic process. Both the crt/optic fibre and the laser approach offer a multiple mixed font and graphics capability which is limited only by the software controlling image generation. Character readers will provide a means of input to the system for existing and future printed material.

Voice recognition systems may eventually replace the keyboard as the principal human interface with the electronic office. The facilities offered appear to be a long way from being useful for free-form text input, but voice recognition could, in the near future, have a great impact by being used to effect a limited range of predefined functions by numeric or single-phoneme commands. In the word processor field 100 editing commands would provide for a wide range of facilities whereas the EMI Threshold voice recognition system already provides for 1000 phonemes.

Voice synthesis facilities in the work-station could be used to provide an audio response to enquiries. The Bank of America currently offer a facility, called BAMTRAC, to its large corporate customers, who through a conventional touch tone telephone can key a coded request to hear an automatically synthesised voice report on their cash balance situation. A combination of voice recognition and voice synthesiser could be used to provide a very natural interface for people to enquire from a corporate or public information base. The 'work-station' in this case needs to be no more than a conventional telephone.

A research team at Queen Mary College, University of London, are developing a management work-station as part of an effort to improve interfaces between man and machine. Their approach to the problems is based on an electronic 'desk top' concept, in which a colour vdu can represent numerous layers of reports, letters and memos. Each of these items is then capable of being extracted and its contents read, manipulated and inserted back within the layers. Additional documents can be searched for and called to the screen thereby permitting comparison, copying and cross-reference of several sources of simultaneously displayed information. The colour graphics is used to aid the human in the comparison process.

Access to other local work-stations will be of prime importance in an electronic office, being used for the internal messages and diary enquiries that keep a business environment alive. This access will be provided by local area communications which will also provide access to central shared facilities, such as archival storage, and also access to external facilities, such as public data networks.

## LOCAL AREA COMMUNICATIONS

Local area communications will offer a simple and flexible approach to connecting high numbers of intelligent devices such as work-stations high-speed printers, data processing computers, telephone handsets, and private branch exchanges. Typically the network could be a loop of wire around an office complex or factory site, with standard sockets at convenient places in the building, probably one by every desk, into which the work-stations could be plugged as necessary. Optic fibre cables are likely to be used when the associated problems are overcome. Such a loop network gives simple control of a high number of devices, currently 256 connections per kilometre.

The control requirements are far less complex than those required for physically extended networks — whether private or public — which have lines radiating from and between controlling computers and devices. The loop network could have considerable installation cost advantages over the conventional network in that what is required to be installed is a single loop of wire compared to a radiating network of wires. However this cost advantage may not exist if an existing internal telephone network were to be used with an advanced private branch exchange acting as a message switching centre between devices. This is discussed in more detail later in this chapter.

The local area networks currently being developed transmit data in packages or messages of a defined structure, thus creating a standard interface requirement for any device connecting to the network. This standard interface gives some degree of device independence. The speed of these networks is another important factor. Currently speeds of 3 to 4 Mbits/sec are being achieved and faster speeds are being worked on. This speed equates to about 150 pages of text per second. Speed such as this will be needed to handle graphics and high volumes of text and data without degrading the performance of any of the terminals.

Such local area networks have been developed by Xerox Corporation (called 'Ethernet') and Cambridge University and are expected to be marketed in the near future. The Xerox 'Palo Alto' advanced office system which is undergoing field trials uses 'Ethernet' as its local communications vehicle. Here 'Ethernet' connects numbers of intelligent work-stations, central xerographic printing facilities and high-volume storage to provide text processing, graphics, personal filing and message facilities.

## CENTRAL FACILITIES

With any electronic office there will be some facilities that have to be shared; this may be dictated by economics or by ease of administration and control. These facilities will be accessed by work-stations through the local area network.

High-speed printing facilities will be required for the bulk information which could not be handled on the quality printer attached to the work-station. Additionally, expensive printers capable of outputting graphic images will also be shared.

High-volume storage for shared information and for archiving of information will be available. Any problems in this area will not be the size of the storage available, but the retrieval methods. Holographic storage and bubble memory will provide the capacity and access time to meet the storage size requirements, but the indexing and the referencing of the information will have to be very flexible to meet the requirements of the informal office activities.

Links with data processing systems will be established to give access to the corporate data base in both an enquiry mode and a data-collection mode. An example of this exists at Texas Instruments in Dallas where the regular data processing reports are generated on central magnetic files in normal report layout image, and the users access the reports from terminals.

Other central facilities are likely to include phototypesetting equipment for the production of high-quality volume printing and microfilm units. Microfilm would be available both as an archival device providing an alternative non-magnetic medium and as a device from which information could be retrieved. Retrieval could either provide data on the work-station which has been coded by a character reader (and hence would then be in a form suitable for manipulation and processing), or has been presented as a digitised image to be looked at by the user but not to be manipulated as text or data.

## PRIVATE BRANCH EXCHANGE (PBX)

Attached to the local area network or in some cases perhaps even controlling it, may be a computer-based private branch exchange (or PBX). The PBX could, in addition to providing advanced voice facilities (such as call intercept, re-route and digitised voice store and forward), also provide the link to the outside world. It may be able to act as a terminal concentrator, controlling the access of work-stations and other devices on the local area network to external facilities. This could include acting as an interface to public data networks.

Rather than interfacing with a local loop network a PBX could act as the central message switch device for a local star network, such as would exist if an electronic office were to be superimposed upon an existing internal telephone network. In this case, the PBX could control all communications, work-station to work-station, work-station to data base, computer to public network, work-station to Prestel, etc. This would be a very complicated control task and if information volumes were high then performance, as judged by a user, could suffer degradation.

## EXTERNAL FACILITIES

The computer-based PBX could give all internal user devices, be they work-stations, central computers or voice handsets, access to external facilities and services. The external facilities being accessed will include voice networks, the capabilities of which will be quite sophisticated. Many of the facilities currently available in the private branch exchange will be available in the public exchanges, so that call re-routeing, re-call-if-engaged and call-last-number-used type facilities would be available across the telephone network.

Access will be available to data networks including the current Public Switch Telephone Network, private networks and the future public data networks. Here we are also talking about the use of specialist timesharing computational services. Public data networks will provide gateways to other private and public networks, both here and overseas. Through this complex of networks a whole range of services will be available.

There are currently the specialist timesharing computational services such as GE ICS, there are computerised data bases containing legal, bibliographic and technical information, such as Lockheed and the Eurospace Agency data bases. The value-added services of some US networks services such as computer conferencing, electronic mail and word processor compatibility services are also accessible through networks in the UK, although currently their use falls foul of data communication rules and regulations.

In addition to access from the dedicated TV-type terminals the Prestel computerised information service provided by the Post Office will be able to be accessed from a local work-station via the PBX, for both the public information and the closed user group information. The Prestel message service, which although designed for the domestic market, will be very suitable for that proportion of business mail which originates from or is destined for private individuals. That portion of mail has been estimated by the West German Postal Authorities to be as much as 47% of total mail volume.[1]

The Telex service as it currently exists has world-wide coverage of the majority of large business organisations, and until other more sophisticated public electronic mail services with equal coverage are established then the electronic office will need access to the Telex network. Teletex is a new text communication system currently being considered by the PTTs across the world through the CCITT. In some sense this could be seen as a super-telex with a larger character set, working at a faster speed and using the PSTN or public data networks, and it could eventually replace Telex. However, Telex is very well established and it will be a long time being replaced.

Faster communications both in-house, as will be provided by local area networks, and in the public domain with the advent of optic fibre and satellite links will make the movement of graphics

[1] Kemp 1978

and images more feasible. Facsimile, line art graphics and video conferencing images will become cheaper to transmit and facilities for this should be accessible through the work-station.

## ARCHITECTURES OF OFFICE AUTOMATION

Some specific electronic office architectures have been mentioned: the local area network and PBX controlled network. Other architectures which can provide some or all of the necessary facilities are described below. There are many variations possible within and between each described architecture. The five main architectures are:

— Stand-alone;

— Shared-resource;

— Timesharing;

— PBX controlled network;

— Local area network.

### Stand-Alone (See Figure 4)

This is a term coined for single work-station word processors. These are capable of operating independently of any other unit, having local processing power, a quality printer, and limited local storage. Such equipment operating alone can only offer limited electronic office facilities, and it can be anticipated that, within the next 5 years, devices without communications facilities will have little appeal. Its capability can be enhanced by using local links to phototypesetting and Telex terminals and by employing character recognition equipment for the input of typed documents.

Links to a central computer can enhance the storage facilities and provide high-speed printing and also give access to the corporate data base. Communications facilities linking stand-alone devices can provide a document- or message-distribution capability. The stand-alone device could become a work-station on the other architectures to be described, thereby giving a wide range of facilities. Examples of such systems are Wordplex 1 and Logica VTS 100, both of which consist of display screen, keyboard, dual diskette drive and quality printer.

### Shared-Resource (See Figure 5)

The term shared-resource is currently used in relation to mainframe-

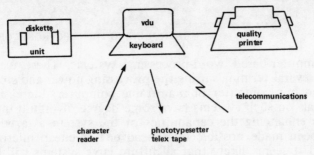

Figure 4   Stand-Alone

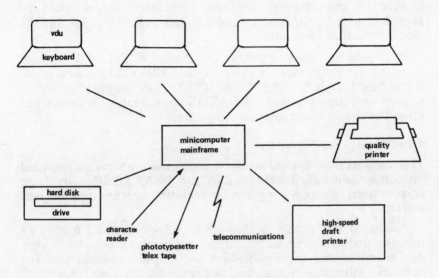

Figure 5   Shared-Resource

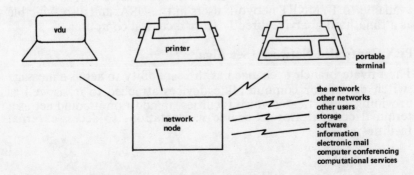

Figure 6   Timesharing

or minicomputer-based word-processing systems. These usually consist of several terminals using the processing power and storage of a shared minicomputer or mainframe computer. Increasingly the terminals on such systems have some degree of inbuilt intelligence thus enhancing the capabilities of the system as a whole. This has been made possible by the advent of cheap microprocessors and it seems likely that all future large systems will have intelligent terminals. The minicomputer will usually be dedicated to the word-processing task whilst a mainframe will normally be performing other computing work. Using any communications facility of the minicomputer or mainframe, access could be gained to timesharing services and data networks, so enhancing the electronic office capability.

Examples of such systems are Wang WPS25 and Unicom (Logica), as minicomputer systems, and IBM's ATMS as a mainframe-based system. The Wang WPS25 can support up to 14 screens and printers. The IBM ATMS configuration is dependent upon the size of the mainframe computer.

### Timesharing (See Figure 6)

This architecture is typified by the timesharing services provided on some value-added networks in the USA. Additionally large corporations are providing similar facilities on their private networks.

Access to the system is through a dial-up terminal facility or through dedicated connections from terminals to network nodes. All inter-terminal communication is via the network, and the network will offer storage and software facilities and interfaces with other networks. The facilities available include document preparation, electronic mail, personal filing and computerised data base access and interactive computing.

An example of such a value-added network service is AUGMENT available to TYMNET network users in the USA, and also available as a timesharing service directly from a central computer.

### PBX Controlled Network (See Figure 7)

The private branch exchange has the capability to act as a message switch centre for computer-like devices attached to it, as well as providing sophisticated voice facilities. In addition it could act as a terminal concentrator to enable work-stations to access external facilities.

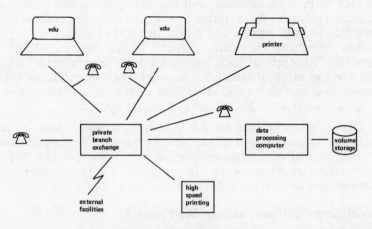

Figure 7  PBX Controlled Network

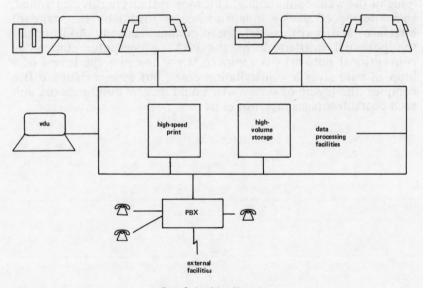

Figure 8  Local Area Network

As a message switch centre it could control the routeing of data or text from work-stations, and use the dp computer printing and storage facilities. As a terminal concentrator it could act as an interface to both private and public networks (including the public switch telephone network, packet switch service, Telex and Prestel). This type of local network could be established utilising the existing internal telephone network of an organisation, thereby minimising installation costs whilst providing access to the network wherever a telephone handset currently exists.

Currently there are no PBXs marketed with these types of facilities. Disadvantages of this architecture are the complex nature of the control of a high number of terminals and the potential degradation of service when high volumes of data are moved about through one central control point.

**Local Area Communications (See Figure 8)**

This architecture was the one that figured in the description of a model electronic office earlier in this chapter. In summary the advantage of this over other architectures is that it offers simple 'plug in the wall' connections. This loop system is easily controlled, some degree of device independence is forced by the standard interface, and it offers high speed communications. Additionally the potential bottleneck of the PBX or computer controlling conventional networks is removed. In a new site the laying of a loop of wire gives low installation costs, but in an existing office complex the laying of such a wire could involve building work and such cost advantages may not exist.

# 3  Products and Services Available

Many of the elements of the future electronic office exist today as individual products and services. Some of these, such as Telex, have been available for a long time and continue to provide a good service. Others such as word processors are the centre of today's office automation activity; whilst some, such as Prestel, are showing more promise than activity.

This chapter indicates the major products and services that are available today and how they may develop in the future. Some of the services mentioned are available in the USA but not in the UK or Europe, mainly because of international data and message transmission regulations rather than any technical or cultural differences.

## WORD PROCESSING

Word processing is receiving greater attention than other aspects of office automation: it is an easy concept to appreciate and its benefits can be seen immediately. The first steps into this area need no large investment and can be made locally in a department or office without requiring the collaboration of other parties.

At its simplest, word processing is an enhancement of the typing function. It can be related to current activities, with the same raw material and finished product: input is in the form of dictation or long-hand manuscript to produce the typed page as output. This is unlike, say, the concept of an enquiry terminal, facsimile transmission or other document communication systems, or an electronic filing system, which all require greater awareness and involvement in a wider work area.

The benefits of word processing can be observed and quantified. A single stand-alone machine can be supplied, plugged into the mains and used immediately with little training. With only corrections and/or replacement text needing to be re-keyed, typists

33

spend far less time in correcting and revising work. A predefined letter can be amalgamated with every entry (or selected entries) on a name-and-address file to produce a 'personal' quality letter for every recipient, with minimum involvement by typists. Contracts produced using standard paragraphs considerably reduce the chance of errors in retyping and simplify the checking of drafts.

## USE OF WORD PROCESSORS

The principal uses of word processing equipment are in the production of:

- one-off documents, short memos;
- regularly-updated reports and manuals;
- standard letters;
- standard documents with the use of standard paragraphs and the inclusion of variables.

In such applications, word processors increase the productivity of correspondence secretaries, whilst at the same time producing a better quality of work and consistency in style. In competitive situations they provide commercial benefits through the production of faster and more accurate reports. Instruction manuals are easier to update and hence can be kept current. The originators of documents are not tempted to compromise on the quality of work because of effort in revision.

In certain locations, a major chemical company has measured the productivity increases which for a mixed typing workload has been found to average up to 100%. The productivity varied depending on the type of work so that for an A4 letter a 15% to 25% increase was observed whilst for multi-format product specifications it was anywhere from 200% to 700%. Productivity gains do depend on the nature of the document and if the opportunity exists for separating the preparation of short memos from the standard letters and regularly-updated reports then productivity benefits can be maximised.

A survey by Unilever of the workloads of their typists before and after the introduction of the Unicom-VTS shared-resource word processors illustrates how the vast reduction in correction and revision time contributes to the productivity increases. The survey was taken over 1200 out of the 24,000 typists in Unilever.

|                              | % Of Total Workload | |
|                              | Conventional<br>% | Unicom-VTS<br>% |
| --- | --- | --- |
| Typing new work              | 20-25 | 60-65 |
| Error correction             | 20-25 | 5 |
| Re-typing (author's revision)| 15-20 | 5 |
| Paper handling               | 5-10  | 0 |
| Idle                         | 30    | 30 |

(The Unicom-VTS is a shared resource system with shared printers, and although the paper handling dropped from 5-10% of workload to 0%, in fact about 3/4 operator/day to serve a pool of 25 typists would be required.)

The facilities which assist in achieving such benefits have some commonality across most of the word processors available. Some of the facilities require external magnetic storage and would not therefore be offered on word processors with internal memory only. The principal editing and processing facilities fall into the following broad categories:

— speeding up the initial text keying and reducing problems of text layout;

— modification of text recorded on magnetic storage;

— use of text recorded on magnetic storage together with keyed text to create a document;

— improvement of printed text quality and the automation of paper handling functions.

## Facilities

*Initial Text Keying*

*Automatic carriage return:* at the end of line, text being keyed is automatically continued at the start of a new line, thereby allowing the operator to key at a uniform speed.

*Automatic underscore:* enables words, titles or text to be automatically underscored.

*Centring:* enables words, titles or text to be automatically centred within specified margins.

*Decimal tabulation:* automatic alignment of columns of figures on the decimal point.

*Forms design:* enables the characteristics of business forms (eg standard letter layout) to be described and stored in the word processor. Each area of the form (eg company name, logo, address, date, margins etc) can be defined in terms of permitted use, thereby avoiding the overprinting of preprinted areas and enforcing the use of a consistent house style.

*Indentation:* enables text to be indented in relation to the left-hand margin and maintains this relationship if the left-hand margin is subsequently changed, such as for the first line of a paragraph.

*Page length control:* enables the number of lines per page to be specified and automatically controlled.

*Right margin justification:* enables text to be automatically aligned to right-hand margins, and for producing an even right-hand margin.

*Subscript/superscript:* enables characters to be above or below the normal text line, eg in chemical formulae.

*Title and page numbering:* enables titles and page number to be automatically generated in a document.

## Modifying Stored Text

*Delete capability:* enables any word, sentence, paragraph or page to be deleted from the storage media.

*Hyphenation control:* enables hyphens inserted for a broken word at the end of a line to be removed automatically if the complete word comes on a single line as a result of subsequent editing. The line-break hyphen is distinguished from the word-structure hyphen, eg brother-in-law.

*Insertion capability:* enables any word, sentence, paragraph or page to be inserted into any portion of the stored text.

*Margination:* enables the position of the right and left-hand margins to be specified with automatic repositioning of the text should the margin positions be subsequently changed.

*Re-pagination:* enables text in a multipage document to be automatically moved to new pages because of additions to, or deletions from, existing text on previous pages.

*Search and replace:* 'search' enables instances of specified text to be automatically located; 'replace' enables each instance of that text to be substituted automatically with new text as specified by the user.

## Use of Text Recorded on Magnetic Media

*Glossary:* enables commonly used words and phrases to be stored and recalled as required by a two or three keystroke reference, eg company names.

*Merge text:* enables the document under preparation to be built up by using text from more than one source, eg keyboard input together with pre-recorded standard paragraphs.

*Qualified selection:* enables selection from files to be made according to parameters specified by the user, eg qualified mailings. The selection can be made using logical include/exclude statements and combiners (and/or) and operators (greater than, less than, equal to, etc).

*Skip capability:* enables selections of text to be unprinted or undisplayed whilst holding it unchanged on magnetic storage for later use.

*Text copy:* enables selections of text to be copied from one stored document into another.

## Print Quality and Paper Handling

*Automatic sheet feed:* enables single sheet stationery to be fed automatically into the printer and positioned at the first line to be printed.

*Proportional character spacing:* enables printed characters to be given space according to their shape and size rather than a fixed space per character, thereby providing higher quality printout.

*Proportional inter-word and inter-character spacing:* enables the spacing between words and between characters in words to be varied automatically to achieve even the right hand margins required on high quality work.

*Variable line spacing:* enables the spacing between lines to be selected.

## STAND-ALONE EQUIPMENT

Word processing facilities are offered in two main forms:

- stand-alone;
- shared-resource.

The stand-alone processor, which is commonly a microprocessor-based unit, is capable of operating independently of the processing and control facilities of any other unit.

Typing is performed through a typewriter-like keyboard which usually has additional command keys to enable word processing to be performed with minimum effort. As the text is keyed, it is usually stored in an internal magnetic memory, at the same time either appearing on paper (as with a standard typewriter) or on a vdu screen enabling the typist to correct immediately obvious mistakes.

The vdus are either partial line displays (say 30 characters), full-line (say 80 characters), partial page (say 24 lines) or full-page (say 70 lines), eg Xerox 850. Partial and full-line displays are often complemented by an automatic line-count display which informs the typist of the current line in relation to the remainder of the text. Partial and full-page displays have an advantage of providing a spatial awareness of the whole text, which can be important as a composition aid. Some word processors have screens that can offer wide displays of 120 or 132 characters per line (eg DEC, Logica). Also offered is the ability to scroll verti-cally and horizontally so that the screen is treated as a 'window', displaying one portion of a larger area of text. Screens displaying either a high number of lines or a large number of characters per line should be studied by prospective users in relation to the size of characters. On displays the characters may be small enough to cause difficulties in the proof-reading of input. The cost of the unit will reflect the features incorporated and the decision on the choice should be based upon the kind of work planned.

After keying on a word processor with internal memory only, the text is committed to paper, but where there is external mag-netic storage the work can be saved there for later printing or modification after checking a draft print.

The magnetic storage types available, together with size and usage are shown in Figure 9, and the printer types are shown in Figure 10.

| TYPE | SIZE<br>1 page = 2,500 chars | USAGE |
|---|---|---|
| internal | one line to 125 pages | short documents, short term storage |
| magnetic card | 2 to 10 pages | short documents, limited revision |
| cassette | 30 to 40 pages | short to medium documents, limited revision |
| data cartridge | 50 to 100 pages | short to medium documents, limited revision |
| minidiskette | 24 to 40 pages | documents of any length, extensive revision |
| diskette | 100 to 200 pages | documents of any length, extensive revision |
| disk | 400 pages upwards | long documents, extensive revision |

**Figure 9.** Typical types of magnetic storage.

Equipment suppliers do not usually offer a choice with a particular model of word processor, and compatability should not be expected between the same type of magnetic storage on different vendors' machines.

| TYPE | SPEED (characters per second) | QUALITY | |
|---|---|---|---|
| golf-ball | 15 | top quality | — impact printer; spherical print head rotates to position the image required; print heads are interchangeable to vary type style. |
| dot matrix | 200 | draft quality | — impact: series of dots forming the shape of the characters; some high resolution printers can give better quality draft; useful for higher-volume work because of speed. |
| daisy wheel | 50 | top quality | — impact: a plastic disk in the shape of a daisy flower head with one character on the face of the 96 petals; the wheels can be interchanged to vary the type style; metallised characters are available for better quality. Dual daisy wheel printers can be used either to handle unusual type fonts (eg scientific) on one wheel, together with a regular type font on the second, or to provide a mixture of common type fonts (eg elite, 14pt bold and italic) to produce a quality of output which could perhaps offer an alternative to much typesetting work. |
| ink jet | 90 | top quality | — non-impact: characters are formed by a controlled jet of quick-drying ink; the character sets and type styles are program-controlled. |

**Figure 10.** Printing facilities which are usually offered.

Daisy wheel printers, usualy Qume (owned by ITT) or Diablo (owned by Xerox), are offered with most stand-alone word processors.

## SHARED-RESOURCE EQUIPMENT

The shared-resource word processor is usually based on a mini-computer which provides processing, storage and printing facilities for several terminals. In this situation, the minicomputer will only perform word-processing functions. Also falling into this category are the mainframe computer-based word processing systems (eg IBM's ATMS) where the mainframe provides the word processing, storage and printing control facilities for connected terminals. In this situation it would be usual for the mainframe computer to be providing other computing facilities in addition to word processing.

Shared-resource terminals, which cannot operate independently of the controlling computer, usually consist of a typewriter-like keyboard and a partial or full-page vdu through which all the word-processing functions could expect to be performed. As costs fall the degree of intelligence present in the terminal is continually increasing, and consequently more functions are being performed at the terminal with the central computer being concerned less with the word processing function and more with printing and storage functions. The magnetic storage in a shared-resource system would normally be disk, controlled by the central computer. The volume of storage available would be subject to the limits of the computer concerned but could reasonably be expected to be 4 million characters (1600 pages) with no practicable upper limit if the system is based on a mainframe.

Shared-resource systems regularly provide a draft print facility via a computer line-printer or dot matrix printer, with a separate machine (daisy wheel, golf-ball or ink jet) for quality output. The printing facilities are usually shared between operators, one person usually having the sole responsibility for print handling.

## PRICE OF WORD PROCESSORS

Figure 11 shows 1979 prices of three typical word processors. One is a non-display word processor, one is display-based and one is a multi-station shared-resource system. The prices in future years will reflect the falling costs of equipment and although the prices shown in Figure 11 are typical of the majority of products today, they are continuously being undercut by new lower cost (and probably higher performance) equipment. Consequently the prices shown should not be taken as a guide to good value for money.

| Model | A. B. Dick Magna II | Wordplex 1 | Wang 30 |
|---|---|---|---|
| Input Display | keyboard 32 char | keyboard/display 24 lines | keyboard/display 24 lines |
| Internal memory | 8,000 char | 48,000 char | minicomputer |
| External magnetic storage | Magnetic Card 5,000 char/ card (2 pages) | Twin diskette drives 256,000 char/drive (100 pages each) | Disk 10,000,000 chars (4,000 pages) |
| Printer | daisy wheel | daisy wheel | 3 daisy wheels |
| Number of keystations | 1 | 1 | 8 |
| Prices | £5,990 | £8,500 | £54,500 |

**Figure 11** Prices of Word Processors (1979)

As in most competitive fields the price of equipment reflects the facilities being bought. This table compares three word-processing systems, each with different features; two of them are stand-alone and one is shared-resource.

## WORD PROCESSING ACTIVITY

It was estimated by International Data Corporation that in December 1977 there were 350,000 word processing units installed worldwide and that world markets were increasing by about 25% per annum, which gives a projected end-of-1979 figure of 555,000. Estimates of the number of UK installations vary from nearly 11,000 (by IDC) to 23,000 (by Mackintosh Consultants) but both agree that the market is expanding by about 25% per annum. Even the 23,000 estimate seems a low figure when compared to the 76,000 Telex installations in the UK but when talking about a new area of activity it is the potential size of the market that is important.

Another indication of activity is that vendors in the UK number well over 50 in 1979 compared with less than 20 in 1976 and new products appear more or less every month.

## WORD PROCESSOR LINKS

The word processor is being linked with other office equipment, eg Telex, phototypesetters, thereby increasing its capabilities. Much effort is being expended by organisations who have the resources to spare, in forging workable links between the word processor and this equipment. But ensuring the compatibility between communication protocols, word processor commands, character sets, magnetic file structures, paper sizes and electrical signals is not the sort of exercise in which the majority of users have the expertise or the money to be involved. Therefore unless the vendors both offer and demonstrate a simple link which can be purchased 'in working order' then the variations in practices and standards across the equipment available will mean that the user will be involved in effort which may be considerable.

The experience of some users who have tried to establish working links between word processors of different makes and between word processors and mainframe computers has not been encouraging. Communications have been effected but for those communications to be useful, then the facilities of the word processor that could be used have had to be so severely restricted, that the word processor was effectively reduced to a buffered terminal, and some of the benefits of having a word processor were lost as soon as communication mode was entered. However, communication between identical models of communicating word processor is now well established and it is something that the user can approach, knowing, having made arrangements with the Post Office for telecommunications facilities, there are few problems and the full facilities of the word processor can be used in the construction of documents for communication.

Links between word processors and other components of the electronic office have been established and are available 'off the shelf'. For example, links with Telex by the production of compatible punch paper tape are available from Vydec. This feature costs an extra £2,750. Included in that facility is code conversion which will cater for the limited Telex character set by expanding special characters as used on the Vydec into several of the Telex characters, eg $ will be expanded to DLR. The use of a word processor-Telex link enables messages to be prepared, corrected and revised using the superior text-preparation facilities of word processors whilst preparing a tape for direct input to the Telex system.

Phototypesetting equipment possesses many of the editing features and facilities of word processors and the operation of inputting is often a duplication of keying effort previously used in preparing the source document. Links between word processors and phototypesetters are available, allowing documents which have been previously prepared on the word processor to be phototypeset with the keying of the typesetting command but not the re-keying of the text. Itek Graphic Products offer an interface which they claim will link most word processors to their Quadritek Phototypesetter. This interface costs £1,250.

Duplicate keying at the stage of inputting to a word processor from a document that is already typed is currently an area of wasted effort. Links between optical character readers and word processors are offered by several wp manufacturers for inputting documents typed in the special OCR fonts, and with developments of microprocessor interfaces by the OCR suppliers availability of such links, are becoming the rule rather than the exception. Vydec text reader (model 761) will accept OCR.B and ECME II characters; this reader costs £11,950 including diskette drive. These readers are currently used on the basis of having 20 to 30 cheap electric typewriters feeding a single expensive word processor on which the corrections and revisions are made. The type font acceptability is being extended so that the bulk of typed material produced today will be input to computer-like systems, without having to make special arrangements for OCR type. (See character recognition section.)

Other links, if not being marketed yet by vendors, are being demonstrated at exhibitions; an example is Xerox who have demonstrated their 850-word processor connected to their very high-speed (5 pages a second) 9700 laser printer. Muirhead's facsimile equipment and Logica's VTS 100 word processor were successfully interfaced at the Hanover Fair in 1979, when text generated by the VTS 100 was output in digital facsimile form.

The links that are established and those that are promised point to the fact that the word processor is the current centre of the electronic office activity and that it could well be the area from which future activity will spread.

## TELEX

When talking about the office of the future it may seem strange to include Telex, a slow old communication system with noisy terminals; however, even though it is old and even though potential replacement services are being discussed (see the section on Teletex later in this chapter), Telex usage is still growing and the service is being enhanced. It will have an important part to play in the early years of the electronic office.

The principal features of Telex as a message system are firstly that the message can be prepared and checked before sending. This means that an operator using the terminal as a paper-tape punch can type the message without using expensive line time in making corrections, and then when the message is seen to be correct, use the terminal as a paper tape reader to read and transmit the message. The second feature is the answer-back facility; this is when the receiving terminal automatically transmits an alphanumeric identity code back to the sending terminal at the start and end of the connection. This confirms both that the message has been sent to the correct place and that the message has been received. The third feature is the auto-answer facility. This permits messages to be received by unattended terminals. The messages are accepted as normal and are printed out as they are received. This facility can overcome problems of variations in working hours caused by time differences across the world.

There are about 1 million Telex installations in the world (source: Post Office); these are used by the majority of large organisations, industrial, commercial and governmental. The Telex networks allow each of those users to contact each other without making prior arrangements and Telex numbers are available from world directories. In most cases contact can be made day or night, thereby avoiding time-zone problems; this is done by utilising the auto-answer facility which is present on most terminals.

It has to be accepted that the system is slow, and that the character set is very limited. Transmission of text is at 50 bits per second (which works out at 5½ characters per second or 66½ words per minute). The character set consists of upper case only A to Z, 0 to 9, 13 special characters and a space. The special characters do not include the £, $, % or fraction signs. Despite these disadvantages Telex has one big thing going for it: it works!

Also it is acceptable for use in financial transactions and the copy is acceptable as a legal record of the message being sent.

The world Telex system, the transmission and the character set are the product of international agreement and compromise between the telephone and telegraph authorities. Before its traffic is attracted elsewhere similar agreements will have to be reached for new services and the new services will have to have the coverage of Telex and the acceptance of the business world. Consequently any move from Telex will be a slow and evolutionary process.

In the UK there are 76,000 installations (1979 figures) and this is expected to grow to 200,000[1] before it levels off in 1988. This is an increase of over 10% per annum for the next 10 years which is a significant growth for an established service. International calls made from the UK are increasing annually at 10% to Europe and 15% to further destinations.[2] International traffic accounts for 40% of the number of Telex calls and for 80% of the duration of calls originated in the UK. However the success rate for connection of international calls is as low as 35%. This high failure rate is composed of subscriber unavailability, international network failures and failure to obtain an international line. In an effort to better this last element, and to cater for increasing international traffic, a programme introducing new international gateway exchanges and new domestic exchanges is being followed by the Post Office. A Plessey 4660/70 computer-based exchange has been installed and this will provide 9000 lines and handle 72,000 calls per hour. It will also offer store and forward facilities, multi-address capability and a retry-if-busy facility. A further exchange using a Plessey 4660/90 is due to be operational in 1981 and this will provide a 37% increase in overseas Telex switching capacity, handling 360,000 calls per hour on 28,000 lines with links to 170 countries. The domestic increase is being planned for by 10 new national exchanges.

## FACSIMILE

Introduced around 1900, facsimile is well established as the most reasonable means for the fast transmission of non-codeable images, and has been used for special applications such as weather map transmission and newspaper photograph transmission for many

[1] Computer Weekly 3 Jan 79
[2] Williamson 1979

years. The introduction of mobile receivers utilising radio transmission has lead to its use in police cars, fire engines, on-board ships and on offshore oil rigs. Over these recent years general business applications have grown until today, it is said that 97% of the top 900 US companies use facsimile.[1]

There were estimated to be 390,000 units[1] worldwide in May 1978, with a 20% growth per annum. The growth rate in Japan, whose language is so unsuited to being coded, is 30%. The popularity of facsimile in Japan is further illustrated by the fact that the ratio of facsimile units to telephones in Japan is twice that in the USA and is four times that in Europe.[2]

Facsimile is a delivery system for copies, where the original is scanned, the image is converted to an electrical signal, which is transmitted to one or more locations where copies of the originals are reproduced. Its use has been justified on speed of delivery, authenticity and labour savings. The range of use has been mostly but not completely limited to intra-company or intra-interest group transmissions, because although there are now some facsimile communications standards, the first of these was not ratified until 1968; secondly there are no directories of users to show who has facsimile equipment and whether it is compatible with yours. In the UK, Rank-Xerox produce a directory of their Telecopier users, and in the USA offer a freephone answering service for the supply of telephone numbers of existing users to other existing users. However, manufacturers usually shy away from producing directories because they represent a ready 'prospect' list for competitors.

For the communication of any information, facsimile has great advantages over communicating word processors in that there are some international standards. These standards have been established by the CCITT and specify details of the facsimile apparatus in three different performance groups. Groups 1 and 2 are for analogue facsimile (the electrical signal varies with the intensity of the image from black to white through greys); and Group 3 is for digital facsimile (the electrical signals represent discrete picture elements of image as either black or white without grey tones).

The types of details specified for Groups 1 and 2 are the scanning line length, scanning density (lines/mm) scanning line frequency (lines/minute) and electrical signal frequencies and durations.

[1] Stamps 1978
[2] Pugh 1978

CCITT recommendation T2 which was ratified in 1968 and modified in 1976 specifies details of Group 1 facsimile apparatus capable of transmitting an A4 size document in 6 minutes.

Recommendation T3 which was ratified in 1976 specifies details of Group 2 facsimile apparatus capable of transmitting an A4 size document in 3 minutes. The information specified for digital facsimile are the picture elements per scanned line, the scanning density in a vertical direction (lines/mm), the scanning line length, the redundancy coding scheme and the electrical signals. Redundancy coding allows strings of all white or all black picture elements to be represented during transmission by much fewer electrical signals than would be necessary if they were not so coded, thus reducing transmission time. The CCITT draft recommendation which was drawn up in 1977 and is due for ratification in 1980 specifies the details of Group 3 facsimile apparatus which is capable of transmitting an A4 size document in 1 minute.

Additional recommendations provide for the 'handshake procedure' which controls the various phases of a facsimile call allowing stations to identify themselves; for the facsimile group (1, 2 or 3) to be agreed; and for the end of messages and message confirmation signals to be passed between stations in a meaningful manner. These details are contained in CCITT recommendation T30. The CCITT recommendations do not cover all the facilities of facsimile devices. Compatible facsimile devices do vary and this could result in a sophisticated device being used in the manner of a very basic device in order that it may transmit to a basic device; in other words, working at the level of the lowest common denominators. However, the facilities now being built into facsimile machines are very sophisticated and include the following:

— paper size selection by transmitter;
— resolution selection/speed selection;
— automatic dialling;
— automatic answer;
— failsafe transmission;
— automatic loaders;
— repeat print of documents;
— light original option;
— encryption facilities;
— filtering of interference.

These facilities provide for the production of good quality copies with the minimum of operation attendance. But these facilities obviously cost money and not all users need them. Allowing for this, the manufacturers see the facsimile market in three categories:

— operational;

— convenience;

— specialised.

Operational facsimile is seen applying to those users for whom more than half of the traffic is of scheduled special-purpose documents, eg daily business reports. In this category, more sophistication is required, particularly facilities such as unattended reception, automatic dialling and automatic loading. Dependent upon the application, the quality of image and paper is not always important.

Convenience facsimile is seen applying to those users for whom unscheduled traffic predominates. Here very little sophistication is required, and the quality of image and paper is usually unimportant.

The specialised facsimile user wants the facilities and the quality not normally associated with general office use. Here we are talking of the military applications of mobile receivers and the transmission of cloud pictures, newspapers and fingerprints.

Three examples of facsimile devices available in the UK are described below. The first would be considered in the convenience market and the last two in the operational market.

- Xerox Telecopier 400: Group 1 (4/6 min)
  Single sheet manual feed
  £29/mth (£825 purchase)

- Plessey MV 1200: Group 2 or 1 (2, 3, 4 or 6 min)
  Unattended operation
  £90/mth (£2,600 purchase)

- Kalle Infotec 6000: Group 3 (35 sec, 1 or 2 min)
  Unattended operation
  Paper size choice
  Filtering of interference
  Repeat print facility
  £7,150 purchase

As a general guide to the selection of the capability of facsimile equipment, one rule is to use the equipment that your traffic volume will keep busy. This strikes something of a balance between costs of equipment and cost of transmission. If a machine is selected which is only used a quarter-of-a-day then the savings on transmission costs will not meet the extra paid to gain that speed of operation.

## Costs of Facsimile Transmission

Transmission costs (in pence) of a single A4 sheet, for greater than 56 km in the UK over the PSTN.

|               | 6 mins | 4 mins | 2 mins | 1 min | 30 sec | 20 sec |
|---------------|--------|--------|--------|-------|--------|--------|
| peak rate     | 108    | 72     | 36     | 18    | 9      | 6      |
| standard rate | 72     | 48     | 24     | 12    | 6      | 6      |

(The transmission costs over the PSTN are an extension of the normal PO rates for telephone usage and are shown at 1979 levels.)

## Facsimile in the Future

The problem of standards and the accessibility of other users is diminishing both because of work in the CCITT and because of the development of facsimile services. ITT Domestic Transmission Inc are about to launch FAX-PAK, a US-wide transmission service which offers compatibility between all 2, 4, 6 and sub-minute terminals. Additional facilities will include a choice of message priority (and presumably tariff), a multiple address facility and an interface to permit telex input. Other value-added networks in the USA such as GRAPHNET also offer conversion services, but FAX-PAK promises to be the most comprehensive.

In Europe the PTTs have plans for facsimile. The British Post Office has published details of a possible customer to customer facsimile service. This service will be initially for Group 2 machines and will allow users to exploit cheap-rate transmission over the PSTN, although transmission at other times will be possible. The machines will scan and store the documents during the day for automatic transmission at night. The service, provisionally called 'Autofax' or 'Nightfax', will use a microprocessor-controlled transmitting station with fast document scanning and storing capabilities and a standard three-minute facsimile receiver.

It is anticipated that the document will be scanned in about 10 seconds and stored together with the recipient's facsimile telephone number on magnetic tape. The device will be automatically switched to 'send' mode by a time clock when the magnetic tape will be read and calls will be automatically established and documents transmitted. Allowing for call set-up time, approximately 15 documents per hour will be transmitted. Transmission failures are logged for interrogation by the operator next morning. Receiving devices which are engaged are automatically re-tried later. A limited Group 2 non-store and forward service, known as Fonofax, has been announced for the London area and will use Siemens' HF 1048 or ITT-Creed transceivers.

Most other European PTTs have plans for or are considering the introduction of facsimile services. The French are looking at the domestic market and in 1978 were aiming for a cheap (1500 francs, £175) high-speed, Group 3 terminal to be supplied in bulk orders at the end of 1980.

International services are being provided or developed. These are mostly transmission from centre-to-centre with hand delivery from the sender to one centre and from the other centre to the recipient. The France-US service, called Teleporte, is expected to provide transmission from Paris to either New York or Washington. Japan and the USA are linked by Q-Fax, a joint RCA-KDD (Kokussai Denshin Denwa Co Ltd) venture which provides for the transmission of documents between the RCA office in New York and the KDD office in Tokyo. Messages received in Tokyo are delivered by hand within Tokyo itself or sent by post. This service, which costs $10 per page, besides providing speed of delivery, avoids the translation and transliteration of Japanese language messages, necessary if existing Roman alphabet-based text services (eg Telex) were to be used.

Facsimile currently exists as one of a number of separate elements of office systems. It starts and finishes as a message-delivery system taking a paper-based image to produce a similar paper-based image, and for many years those have been its limits. However, the developments which are bringing together the other elements of office systems are also embracing facsimile and making it part of the integrated electronic office.

The areas of integration that can currently be seen include the development of a combined optical character reader/facsimile reader (Omnifax) by Stewart Warner in the USA and more recently by Muirhead in the UK. With this device, areas of image that can be recognised as specific characters are stored as code; otherwise the areas are stored as digitised image. Not only does this technique reduce transmission time for conventional facsimile-type activity, but it also opens up possibilities for the storage and processing of mixed image and text documents in information systems.

The Stewart Warner device was only a prototype and is unlikely to be marketed in its current form,[1] but reports are that the Muirhead device is likely to be the first Omnifax product. The development of laser printers and crt-based image printers (see Chapter 2) which are capable of printing multi-font characters and digitised images provides the basis for the multi-purpose facsimile and text printers, and the use of amalgamated image and coded text information. Although not using coded text, a facsimile device has been used as the printer for a word processor. Digitised text from a word processor was output on a facsimile printer at the 1979 Hanover Fair when Logica's VTS100 word processor was linked to a Muirhead digital facsimile device.

The developments in character recognition and image printers, the fact that images and text are so often mixed together in business communication, and that images are an important part of business, give facsimile a firm place as one element of an integrated electronic office.

## INFORMATION BASES

The changes in the cost-performance relationship in both computing and telecommunications have brought about the establishment of many on-line information bases available for public access. These information bases cover mostly scientific, technical and bibliographic material. Unlike the Prestel information this material is mostly static and is supplemented rather than amended. The producers of the basic information are in most cases not primarily in the business of selling information, eg the Chemical Society of America *(Chemical Abstracts)*, the Institution of Electrical Engineers *(Science Abstracts)* and NASA. These information producers will supply their files to an information supply service who will set up the means of access and sell the on-line search and retrieval of the information to end-users.

Some principal information supply services available from within the UK are: British Library Automated Information Service (BLAISE), European Space Agency — Space Documentation Service, General Electric, Lockheed Information Systems, and

[1] Anderson 1978

Systems Development Corporation Search Service. Between them, access is available to approaching 100 on-line information bases, which cover areas from the characteristics of electrical components, *Metal Abstracts Index* and *Chemical Abstracts,* to the British National Bibliography.

Access to the data bases is effected by the use of terminals on dedicated lines, or more popularly by the use of terminals connected by dialling over the PSTN. Use of a dedicated line is warranted where the volume of enquiries is high. The cost of the telephone lines, either dedicated or dial-up, can be a significant part of the cost of retrieval. Because of this, some services provide a network with a series of nodes in major centres, thereby reducing the user's line-cost element of the total cost of retrieval, and also providing more reliable telecommunications.

BLAISE, for example, has nodes in Birmingham, Edinburgh, London and Manchester, and has additional nodes planned for Bristol and Boston Spa (National Lending Library) which will give over a third of the existing users access at local phone call rates.[1] An example of the cost of using such services is, for BLAISE, a £25 annual subscription and a £25 per hour connect-time usage charge (excluding telephone line charges). The simplest kind of terminal needed would cost around £400. Typical enquiry costs would be £25 per 50 citations.

The Lockheed, General Electric and SDC services are based predominantly on US-held data bases. General Electric Limited has its own worldwide network (GEICS) with several access nodes in the UK. Lockheed and SDC are accessed through the London node of TYMNET, the Tymshare network, which provides the transatlantic link necessary to use the data bases.

In 1976 agreement was reached within the EEC to provide a European information network: EURONET-DIANE (Direct Information Access Network for Europe) to meet the need and growth of traffic accessing information bases. This would also reduce the reliance on US-held information. The information service, opened in 1979, is controlled by the European Commission who contracted the PTTs to provide the network. Euronet has 9 nodes, and will be capable of providing interconnection with national networks both within and without the EEC, eg the UK's

[1] Collinge 1978

Packet Switched Service (PSS) and then via PSS to IPSS and via RCA or Western Union to TYMNET into the USA. But the regulatory aspects are complex and it cannot be deduced that access in the reverse direction (from TYMNET to EURONET) will be allowed.

Several factors are now influencing the growth in use of on-line information bases to the extent that the facility to access such information is likely to be provided as one of the functions of the electronic office work-station of the technical and professional worker. These factors are the growing use of similar equipment and concepts at a different level (eg word processors, Prestel), which serve to increase familiarity and acceptance of the ideas.

Networks are making the various information bases more easily accessible. The information bases are also becoming more comprehensive the longer they are in existence. In consequence they are becoming more attractive to the user. These factors are combining to make available a growing use of (and a growing number and variety of) information bases. A factor which could complicate information retrieval in the future is the possibility of transnational data flow regulations. These regulations could treat information in a similar manner to valuable goods and subject them to import and export controls and tariffs.

## PRESTEL

Prestel is a Post Office service facilitating access to information stored on regionally distributed computers. Access to the information can be gained through a modified domestic TV set and an ordinary telephone. The service was designed as a low-cost and easy-to-use information system, giving a powerful tool to millions of people. The first public service (initially restricted to the London area) commenced in the first quarter of 1979 and the Post Office project figures of 3 million users by 1983, of which 20% are expected to be business users.

The nature of the terminal can be a special domestic television (colour or black and white) with either a numeric or an alpha-numeric keypad and a dial or push-button telephone. This would be the normal household set-up, with the TV still being capable of receiving the normal broadcast programmes.

Using the numeric keypad, instructions are given by selecting numbered options offered on the screen, whereas the alpha-numeric keypad would enable more complicated procedures and free-form messages to be specified. Special low-cost business terminals are developed for the office environment. These will incorporate keypads and special keys. For use in public places coin-in-the-slot Prestel terminals have been developed. Intended for use in libraries, shops, airports, railway stations, hotels, etc, this type of terminal will make the Prestel services available to many more people, whether or not they are listed Prestel users.

Users of Prestel can either be individuals with access to the public information which is available to all, or they can be part of a closed-user group where, in addition to the public information, access is also permitted to information restricted to members of that group. This would be suitable for a supplier giving information on goods to established customers or for internal company use.

The cost of accessing information will have three elements; the cost of the phone call to the computer centre; a rate charge for use of the service; and a charge per frame as decided by the information provider. The current charge for the use of the service is 2p per minute.

Information providers rent frames from the Post Office. Each frame will hold up to 960 characters using seven colours and providing for simple line diagrams. The information providers can use the frames as they wish and nominate the charge they wish to be made to users who access the frame. The Post Office collect these charges from the users for the providers. Information providers complete the frames from an editing terminal, although the facility for computer generation of frames of data is envisaged for the larger provider. The charges for information providers are, in 1979, £4,000 per year plus £4 a frame.

The type of information being held on Prestel includes general information such as news, sports, timetables, entertainment guides, career guides, financial guides and secretarial services. Publishing organisations figure quite strongly in the information providers and use Prestel as a medium for static information. However, it is anticipated that the proportion of more regularly updated information will increase as users begin to use Prestel for other than the receipt of information. Prestel can have facilities for the ordering of goods (mail order) or the requesting of further details or requesting representatives to visit. Details concerning the paying for ordered goods by credit card over Prestel are being arranged. Message facilities are part of the future plans for Prestel. Using a store and forward concept, messages will be stored at the local Prestel computer centre with an indicator at the receiving terminal to say that a message is waiting. In this way messages can be communicated without both parties having to be available at the same time.

Computational facilities for standard business problems using the processing power of the local Prestel computer are planned. In this situation the system could perform say cash-flow calculations interactively with the user. The connection of microcomputers to Prestel to act as information-provider terminals and as user terminals increases the scope tremendously. This type of device has memory and storage so that information requested from the system could be stored, and could then be processed in the terminal. The storage of computer programs as information frames on Prestel could provide the microcomputer terminal user with a whole selection of application programs and the software house with a reliable distribution and advertisement channel.

The use of microcomputers as viewdata terminals brings us to the question of Prestel being one of the functions available on the electronic office work-station. Prestel appears to be an important part of the future of information provision and the ability to access that information and bring it into the organisation's information system without expensive transcription will be necessary. Prestel is new and is not yet in full service. There are no technical reasons why the described facility should not be available in the future.

An alternative to the Post Office Prestel service is the private viewdata service which could be set up for in-company use or to replace a Prestel closed-user group. Software is available from GEC for use on Data General Nova and Eclipse machines. The use of such a system could dramatically reduce the costs to companies wanting to establish in-house or wider closed-user group viewdata services and the Post Office has no objection rival services being established. This system functions just like any computer-based information network, with the differences that modified TV sets and the software design provide an interface which is easier for the non-technical user to accept than the conventional computer terminal interface.

## PUBLIC DATA NETWORKS

Currently, data communication can be effected over the Public Switched Telephone Network (PSTN) or over lines leased from the Post Office. The PSTN offers the flexibility of being able to vary the destination of the call, and the charge is based on usage. The leased lines are dedicated to a specific route and the charge is fixed irrespective of usage. Both the PSTN and leased lines are using facilities which are designed primarily for voice and we make the best job of them we can for data. The leased lines, being of a single route, can be conditioned to make them better for data, but the PSTN by its nature cannot be conditioned and it suffers all the interference consequent of exchange switching.

Hence the guaranteed data speeds available on PSTN are much lower than on leased lines. One thing both have in common is that the service provides a basic facility for transmitting electrical signals. This means that the responsibility for making sure that the equipment at either end of the line talks the same language at the same speed, and follows the same protocols, is that of the user and equipment manufacturer. Hence all data communications can only be made after thoughtful exclusive relationships have been established between the users. This, for specific applications and for large volume intra-company movements of traffic is acceptable. But for low-volume inter-company communications where the time scales or economics do not allow compatibility to be established, the PSTN and the leased line options are not satisfactory.

Public packet switched data networks are currently being planned or implemented in several European countries (see Figure 12). With these networks we are talking about networks designed for data rather than voice, and networks based on the principle of sharing of resources and thereby giving a high performance and a higher utilisation than leased lines and theoretically lower costs. There will be a common interface definition (X25) which will enforce a certain level of machine independence and thereby facilitate easier user to user connection. The X25 interface definition itself only partially fulfils computer/terminal compatibility requirements, and the implementation of full compatibility standards is not likely to be effected in less than a 5-10 year time period.

The P.O. are engaged in a programme of phased implementation of a digital network (system X) capable of transmitting voice, data, text and image. This is scheduled for introduction in the mid-1980s, and on that, network packet switching will be just one of a range of public services available from which users will select according to their need.

It is the intention that PSS should be the mandatory form of access to EURONET, TRANSPAC and other public data networks and is a possible vehicle for Teletex and Prestel information providers and other services. Access could then be available to all users of the network and to users and facilities on other networks, both private and public, national and international.

This degree of accessibility has not been available before on data transmission services, and its true worth will take time to be realised and exploited, even though such accessibility is accepted and even expected of the voice telephone service. Having said that, other characteristics of the voice telephone service, where 80% of the UK's 22 million phones have direct dialling facilities to 325 million phones in 57 countries (or 80% of world phones), also need to be applied to advanced public data networks; that to be useful to most electronic office users there needs to be many users on the network, ie the network must have good coverage; also the network must be capable of handling the traffic that will be generated by a large number of users. Without that capacity the networks can only offer an alternative transport mechanism for those existing leased-line and PSTN users.

**Figure 12**   European Public Packet Switch Networks.

|  | Coverage | | | |
|---|---|---|---|---|
|  | centres | intermediate nodes | terminals either 1978 or on opening if later | avail-ability |
| Belgium | 3 |  | 1000 | 1980/81 |
| France (TRANSPAC) | 18 |  | 2200 | 1978 |
| Italy | 3 |  |  | 1981 |
| Netherlands (DN-1) | 3 | 62 | 1400 | 1979/80 |
| Nordic (NPDN) Denmark, Sweden, Norway, Finland | 4 |  |  | 1981 |
| Spain (RETD) | 5 | 30 | 8600 | 1971 |
| UK (PSS) | 3 | 6 | 473 | 1979/80 |
| UK International Packet Switch Service (IPSS) (gateway to other networks) | 1 |  | 84 | 1978 |
| W Germany | 7 | 30 | 2000 | 1979/80 |
| EEC (EURONET) | 4 | 5 | 176 | 1979 |

(Information extracted from *Plans of the European Telecommunications Administrations,* CEPT 1978.)

## VALUE-ADDED NETWORK SERVICES

Value-added network (VAN) services are services that do more than merely transmit information. In one way or other they manipulate, translate, re-order or store information on behalf of the sender or recipient. In the USA this type of service is in extensive use and the demand is expanding. In 1977 it was estimated that the market for value-added network services for data, text and images was $50 million, growing at 40 per cent per annum.[1]

In the US, VAN services are run by organisations from a variety of backgrounds who, using the basic data-carrying facilities of the telephone and data transmission companies (common carriers), offer additional facilities. The backgrounds of the VAN companies include computer service-vending for Tymshare, international communications for ITT, railways for Southern Pacific Communications Company, national telephone services for AT & T and telex/telegram for Western Union Telegraph Company.

In the UK and Europe, telecommunication regulations are such that only the PTTs (Postal and Telephone and Telegraph Authorities) can offer many of the VAN facilities as a public service. VANS are allowed to operate in parts of Europe, but under restrictive conditions. They are not allowed to offer third-party switching or other services over which the PTTs claim monopoly supply. The only VAN services currently offered by the PTTs are the national packet switched services. An envisaged VAN service is 'Teletex', the text communication service at present under discussion at CCITT. The facilities offered by the US VAN services are being increasingly used. It remains to be seen whether, in the future, PTTs east of the Atlantic will react to demand and provide the services themselves or will relax their position and allow other organisations to use the PTTs basic communications services to provide those currently prohibited services.

The range of facilities offered by VAN services include:

— packet switching;
— store-and-forward, and polling;
— compatibility (of equipment and networks);
— interactive timesharing and remote job entry;
— support services.

[1] Lurin 1978

This list includes packet switching which is more communications than computing, and interactive timesharing which is more computing. However, both fall within the scope of value-added network services.

Packet switching requires little effort to use and is highly reliable. It should provide an easy way into data communications for a user and a low-cost way of establishing a network. But in the UK at least, until suitable off-the-shelf products are available, the connection and interfacing costs and the ease-of-use will be uncertain.

Store-and-forward and polling services help the control of information flow. These are particularly useful in applications with large terminal populations, such as electronic mail and credit checking and also help to overcome dependence on availability of recipient.

Compatibility services allow dissimilar terminal equipment (including facsimile, text editing and data terminals) to communicate by providing speed, code format, data structure and protocol conversion. These services allow users to use wide ranges of terminals in their systems. This flexibility can be extremely important to users who want to avoid being 'locked in' to a particular manufacturer, and who want to allow the various end-user functions of an organisation to control their own terminal acquisitions. The importance of this flexibility is illustrated by the fact that the average *Fortune* 500 company in the USA has over 800 terminal devices.[1]

Interactive timesharing and remote job entry are complementary to the VAN services mentioned above and allow the user to have complete computing and communications facilities available through a single network. Joint text editing/message distribution facilities, and information base search facilities and statistical computation facilities are examples of these types of services.

Support services are used primarily to help users in the operational aspect of the communications network. These include fault location and fault diagnosis services, management statistics on network usage and personnel training services as part of the VAN facility.

(Fortune 500: the top 500 US manufacturing industry companies as listed by the *Fortune* magazine.)

[1] Lurin 1978

The VAN services give the user:

- *high reliability,* achieved by using redundant circuitry, alternative routeing and sophisticated error-correction techniques in the network;
- *economy,* offered by virtue of the efficient utilisation of transmission media and distance insensitive pricing;
- *compatibility,* offered for interfacing wide varieties of terminals and computers;
- *flexibility,* given in the choice of terminals, in adding new locations and applications and in increasing traffic volumes without the user having to reconfigure networks.

Application of the VAN services is found in the following areas:

- data base and information base access;
- electronic mail services both intra- and inter-company;
- remote computation facilities;
- data collection;
- text editing and information filing;
- computer conferencing;
- credit checking and other financial transactions.

From the list of applications it can be seen that VAN services are now providing users with the capabilities of a full electronic office. As the number of users and the number of network interconnections increase, those capabilities will be used to greater effect.

Facilities of some US value-added networks can be used from the UK. Both Tymnet and Telenet have nodes in London. These were opened essentially to give easier access to the large information bases resident in the USA. Regulations in the UK do not permit these networks to be used for electronic mail or for computer conferencing, and although there are no technical problems in using these facilities, use is restricted to the information access and remote computing services.

To illustrate the facilities of VAN services, three example networks will be discussed: TYMNET, an existing packet switched network for data and text; FAX-PAK, a facsimile network; and ACS, a proposed packet switch service from AT & T.

TYMNET is owned by Tymshare a major US computer service vendor and the network was created initially to supply its own needs for communications services. TYMNET now offers the following:

- local call access available from 150 cities in US;
- compatibility services for 100 different terminals;
- interfacing of 50 computer models for 15 manufacturers;
- data base access facilities are available;
- network interconnection via international carriers exists and interconnection with new national data networks is planned;
- access to the network and sections of the network is restricted to authorised users.

Also available to TYMNET users is ON-TYME, a store and forward electronic mail service; PLANET/FORUM, a computer conferencing system; and AUGMENT, a document preparation, distribution and filing system. These TYMNET facilities offer one provision of the electronic office.

FAX-PAK, a US-wide facsimile-compatibility network to be offered by ITT Domestic Transmission Systems Inc, is due to start operation late in 1979. It will be based upon packet switching and will offer a high degree of reliability and economy. Universal compatibility among 2, 4, 6 minute and sub-minute facsimile machines is to be provided. Compatibility with Telex and various data terminals used as input devices will be available. Three delivery options will be offered: immediate (within 15 minutes), four hours, and overnight. Other features offered are multiple addressing, acknowledgement of receipt, and directory services. Price is distance-insensitive and varies only with use.

Of special significance is the proposal of AT & T to establish an Advanced Communications Service (ACS) because this offers some guidance on the future shape of public services elsewhere. Because the proposal involves AT & T operating outside its currently-defined boundaries by providing data processing services in addition to basic transmission, the proposal is currently awaiting approval by the federal regulatory agencies. The plans are very ambitious and are based upon a forecast of 15-18 million terminals in use by 1990 and a revenue to ACS approaching $500 million by 1983.[1]

[1] White 1979

The following are the major features of ACS:

— It will offer a store and forward network service using a wide range of transmission techniques, and would connect to the nodes of the existing Bell network.

— It is intended to satisfy the needs of a wide range of users as a public service comparable to the telephone service. The network will perform interfacing and protocol conversion functions so that there should be almost complete freedom of interconnection of a wide range of computing and terminal equipment — something like 450 terminal models supplied by 100 manufacturers are covered.

— In addition it will offer services such as: text editing, message switching and data collection functions.

Clearly, because of AT & T's dominant position as the major supplier of trunk circuits, ACS, if approved, will become a significant force. The proposal has provoked considerable opposition from other Value-Added Carriers and also from IBM through their stake in Satellite Business Systems. It could also have implications for suppliers of communications equipment like multiplexers, concentrators and modems because ACS (in common with other networks employing packet switching principles) will replace many of the functions performed by this equipment. In addition since it seems likely that ACS will be providing appropriate interfacing products, it could also be a major purchaser of minis and micros.

The PTTs (including the UK PO) are keeping very close watch on the progress of ACS. There have been indications that a number of them acting through CCITT are definitely interested in extending their role to include the provision of value-added services.

## ELECTRONIC MAIL SYSTEMS

This section considers Electronic Mail Systems, ie systems which distribute addressed messages. The simple connection of two word processors does not fall within the idea of electronic mail. It may be electronic message communication but lacks the essential feature of the message being addressed.

The addressing of the message is the characteristic that allows the system to perform the delivery of the message, without the sender having to establish contact with the recipient before the message is despatched. In most cases the messages are handled using a store and forward concept, with messages being delivered to 'electronic post boxes' from which the recipient retrieves the messages when convenient.

Electronic mail systems have been developed for a number of years by large organisations utilising their own intra-organisation networks. In the early days, many of the systems utilised teletype technology on dedicated telegraph grade networks. Subsequent implementations have seen internal systems superimposed onto the general data communications network and thereby offer many more facilities than the teletype approach. Examples of this type of approach are found in Texas Instruments and Bank of America. Texas Instruments has a distributed minicomputer network and additional facilities spanning four continents and including 52 distributed computing nodes. In addition to the corporate data processing activity there is an electronic mail system which can direct messages to any terminal or printer on the network. In 1979 it was reported that 21,000 messages a day are handled on the network at a per message cost of 6c to 8c per destination for a 800-character message.

The Bank of America has a worldwide Interactive Computing Facility network, with over 2,000 individual users. This network was developed to provide interactive timesharing facilities such as financial modelling, statistical analysis, data base enquiry facilities and text editing, but also includes electronic mail communication available for all users of the network.

Those two examples were of very large organisations who had the opportunity to use existing networks; the majority of users are not in that situation. An alternative to building your own network and writing your own software is to use a proprietary system for in-house electronic mail. These are mostly based upon established computing products and do offer an easier way of establishing a dedicated electronic mail system. For example IBM's Text Routeing System links together IBM Office System 6 machines in a star network through a Series 1 computer. Here the text processing capabilities of the Office System 6 can be fully utilised together with the Series 1 providing store and forward facilities for addressed messages.

Electronic mail services provided by outside organisations do exist on value-added networks in the USA. In Europe the PTTs do not provide such services but are currently discussing Teletex, a text communication system, in CCITT. Of the VAN service electronic mail systems, perhaps On-Tyme is the best example, being in operation and fairly representative of others planned.

On-Tyme uses the TYMNET packet switched network as its principal communications resource and hence gains the benefits of terminal independence, high reliability and economy. Store and forward message switching technology is used, giving flexibility and control to the message application.

The functions of On-Tyme are listed below (this forms a comprehensive reference list of electronic mail functions[1]):

— verifies authorised use at log-in;

— allows user enquiry of message status;

— provides optional on-line message preparation and editing;

— all messages are given a time and date stamp;

— all messages are assigned a unique master message number;

— the message is held for the receiver to collect or the system attempts to deliver the message (user's choice);

— an output sequence number is assigned at time-of-delivery;

— delivers to group coded destinations;

— responds with error messages to users, as appropriate;

— provides on-line file storage for frequently-used text or data;

— holds all messages three days for on-line retrieval;

— archives messages on tape for 90 days;

— provides traffic analysis data for management control.

The 1978 costs of using On-Tyme include a $100 per month service charge and then a distance-insensitive usage charge. The usage charge is constructed from a connection to TYMNET rate, a charge rate for characters transmitted, a flat-rate message per destination charge and a customer data storage charge. As an example a 500-character message sent using 300 character-per-second terminals would cost $0.23 to send and $0.09 to receive: a total of 32c for the message.

On-Tyme using TYMNET overcomes the problems of incompatible terminals by providing compatibility services. Users accept that the compatibility service is one of the most important features of such networks and are prepared to pay for that service. Another

[1] Field 1977

approach to providing compatibility is to provide a service which quite rigidly dictates the characteristics of the terminals using the service, and then somehow to make that service attractive enough for users.

The CCITT is currently engaged in discussions on the specifications of a worldwide text-communication service, Teletex. This service could become attractive to the user because of economy or because of the worldwide coverage and high number of users or simply because there is no alternative service (particularly in Western Europe). The proposals under discussion are being based upon a definition of the characteristics of a Teletex terminal and its interface with any communications network. Plans are that Teletex proposals will be ratified at the 1980 plenary session of CCITT. The following is extracted from a draft CCITT recommendation dated November 1978.

'With the aid of a TELETEX terminal it is possible to produce character-coded texts and to transmit their true contents and form to a receiving terminal.

- A TELETEX terminal, operating in the local mode, can also be used like a typewriter to prepare ordinary office documents. By means of the TELETEX communication facilities, the text thus prepared can be transmitted to other TELETEX terminals or received from them.

- The TELETEX terminal allows text to be communicated from any subscriber to any other subscriber.

- All terminals all over the world participating in the TELETEX service have to be compatible with one another at a basic level.

- In order to support a high grade of service, a transmission rate of 2.4 kbit/sec on the subscriber line wherever possible. Detailed arrangements on a national level are left to Administrations concerned.

- When operated in the local mode, eg when the TELETEX terminal is used in the same way as an office typewriter, the local mode operation must not be interrupted by incoming traffic.

- The terminal has the ability to generate graphic and control characters of the basic international TELETEX repertoire.

- The terminal must have the ability to present all graphic characters of the basic international TELETEX repertoire.

- The terminal has the ability to respond to the control characters of the basic international TELETEX repertoire.

  However, additional character sets of the TELETEX graphic character repertoire — other than the basic international TELETEX graphic characters — may not be capable of being received by all TELETEX terminals.

- The page is the basis for text formatting and text transmission.

- The terminal can handle paper size A4.

- A printable area of the page is defined within which free positioning of the text is possible during local text preparation.

- After transmission, the content, layout and format of a TELETEX message must be identical at the transmitting and the receiving terminals, when using the defined basic mode of TELETEX operation.

- The TELETEX terminal must be provided with storage for transmitting and receiving functions.

- The TELETEX terminal must provide means for automatic calling, transmission and clearing functions. For the purpose of automatic operation, an internationally agreed unique subscriber identification must be provided.

- The basic TELETEX terminal should provide the capability of interworking with telex.

- It is the responsibility of Administrations to decide in which network the TELETEX service is provided.

- Each call shall include a call identification, which should contain the following information:

  - unique identification of the originating terminal;

  - unique identification of the desired receiving terminal;

  - date and time of transmission of the information (eg in the format YYYY-MM-DD-HH:MM);

  - page number and/or total number of pages (eg in the format xx(yy) );

  - a daily message serial number (optional), and

  - a private field.

- The terminal shall be equipped with a nationally unique identification code that can be released on demand by the calling party, or, for control purposes, by the network.
- Since the effectiveness of the Teletex service will be increased by the availability of special facilities such as those given in the list of examples below, Administrations should give attention to their early introduction.
  - storage in the network (eg delayed delivery);
  - abbreviated address calling;
  - multi-address calling;
  - line identification by the network;
  - automatic date and time indication;
  - indication of charge.
- Provision should be made in the network so that applications such as information retrieval, remote editing and encryption are possible.'

Even though the Teletex service is still very much under discussion and undergoing continuous refinement, the type of service likely to emerge can be seen from those extracts from draft recommendations. The international Teletex character repertoire which is being proposed will be far more extensive than the international alphabet number 2 used with Telex. As currently proposed it will include A to Z, both upper and lower case, 0-9, and 59 other special characters, diacritical marks, accents, and special letters, the latter including diphthong, sharp s, section mark and paragraph mark.

The manifestation of the Teletex terminal is not defined, nor is its function as an office machine. It could be a dedicated Teletex terminal or it could be a word processor or an electronic office work-station. What is important is that its characteristics are being defined so that every user in the world will be able to communicate with every other user, and that it is intended that there will be many users. The definition of characteristics also leaves the choice of networks to the national administrations. The implication of this is that, unlike Telex, the Teletex service will be network-independent so that a variety of existing networks can be utilised: analogue, digital, packet switch, etc. This removes the need for massive engineering projects and will thus speed up implementation.

At first it may appear to be only a super-Telex, having a larger character set, operating at a faster speed, and producing more presentable output. The special facilities such as the store and forward and multi-address calling suggested for consideration, start to establish this service as true electronic mail with facilities matching those of On-Tyme, yet with the backing of international agreement and access to a user base many times larger than On-Tyme could hope to achieve.

For many organisations, particularly the small heavily communicating sort, eg freight agents, Teletex is likely to be the first step into office automation. The introduction of word processing in its own right has been hard to justify in many small organisations where opportunities for staff savings have been minimal. However, when combined with a communication service such as Teletex, a joint word-processing communications system can become feasible.

## CONFERENCING SYSTEMS

Substitution for travel to meetings of two or more individuals or groups is the common theme running through all conferencing systems. Some systems do just that, whilst other systems will enhance the capabilities of those involved in the conference by providing the participants with access to information and computation facilities. The disadvantage common to all conferencing systems is the removal of face-to-face contact.

The main types of conferencing systems are:

— voice conferencing;

— video conferencing — continuous;

— video conferencing — snapshot;

— computer conferencing — screen sharing;

— computer conferencing — file sharing.

Voice conferencing facilities are available on many modern private branch exchanges through the existing telephone handsets. Similar multi-port conference facilities are also a possibility for the future when Stored Program Exchanges are introduced to the national telephone network. For more formal meetings audio conference facilities can be rented and set up to provide good quality sound transmission between several groups of people. Voice conferencing does offer some personal contact, but leaves no opportunity for the convenient exchange of written information and facts and figures during the conference.

Video conferencing with continuous television pictures and sound of other parties is offered by the British Post Office under the name of Confravision. The Confravision service links several studios in major cities in Britain. In addition mobile studios are being introduced to enable organisations to set up longer-term conferences from on their own premises. This service gives the opportunity of displaying documents and charts on the screens during the conference. In this vision-and-sound conferencing a bit more personal contact can be established between members of the meeting than with voice conferencing alone.

Video conferencing with a continuous picture requires high speed transmission lines, which all potential users will not have available. An alternative system which can still give a degree of visual contact and is very suitable for documents is the snapshot video. With snapshot video, single frame pictures are transmitted as required using the speed capabilities of existing transmission facilities. The snapshots could take say 15-20 secs to be transmitted and built up on the video screens. This system is adequate for document and chart display and can be used on existing communications lines, although there is less personal contact than with the continuous video.

Computer conferencing utilising shared terminal screen images is a facility which when supplemented by voice conferencing can be a powerful tool. All members of the conference have a terminal screen of text/data which can be amended and discussed as desired. Such a service is available as part of the AUGMENT system marketed by Tymshare in the USA. This conferencing method using the processing power of computer systems additionally allows users to save copies of screens in various states, to reference information bases and to use text editing facilities to develop contributions in private.

The conferencing systems mentioned so far all offer a substitute for travel to meetings but none offer a substitute for the inconvenience of all members having to be available at the same time. In large organisations time-zone differences can cause problems by creating very short time-slots for convenient conference times. The difficulties in finding mutually convenient dates for meetings can create a lead-time for meetings of weeks or even months, and even though a quickly organised meeting would have been preferable from the business point of view, a delay is unavoidably created.

Computer-based conferencing, which offers the opportunity for non-simultaneous interaction, provides an answer to these types of problems. These systems permit effective contribution of a number of people to continuing work programmes at their own convenience. Such continuing programmes could, conventionally, require meetings at fortnightly intervals for several months, and during that time period it is likely that meetings are missed by people for a variety of reasons. Consequently decisions are made and topics are discussed without all members being involved; whereas a computer-based conference would ensure that all members had a reasonable opportunity to contribute to the discussions and to record their opinions.

Computer conferencing systems are available on Value-Added Networks in the USA. The PLANET/FORUM system is marketed by Tymshare Inc, and can use the TYMNET packet network as the basis for its telecommunications. Such a system would probably be used to provide a number of conference facilities:

- conferencing;
- messages;
- personal notebook;
- notice board.

Conferencing will be facilitated by the use of a common space where a group of users can hold a common discussion on a topic and maintain proceedings for later reference. This type of activity can be simultaneous, or it can be non-simultaneous with users entering and retrieving text and data at their own convenience. When people join or rejoin a continuing conference a transcript of the entries made in their absence is made available.

Messages to and from individual users can be made in 'private' outside of the common forum. Again these messages can be sent and collected as convenient.

A personal notebook space can be used for creating and revising possible contributions to the common conference. Access to sections of one's personal notebook may be granted to other individuals in the conference so that comment can be received and acted upon or so that co-author submissions can be developed.

A notice-board space could be available for items and reports of current interest which are not properly part of the subject under discussion in the conference.

Servicing those four main facilities, there will also be text editing to help authors to compose and correct messages and contributions. Indexing will assist in the searching and retrieving of entries in a number of ways, eg by date, author, subject. Cross-referencing to earlier entries will allow dialogues to be followed through a whole conference. Information base access and computational facilities will supplement the conferencing process by giving all users access to specialist information and specialist services at any time in the conference.

The facilities discussed above are capable of doing far more for people than merely substituting for travel and allowing non-simultaneous meetings. They are providing a tool with which new opportunities can be created. The potential can be illustrated by a wide range of specific suggestions[1], as made in 1974 at the International Conference on Computer Communications. This list of . suggestions included:

- A group of salesmen involved in marketing a line of technical equipment maintains a continuous conference for the purpose of comparing responses to customer questions and analysing competitive products.

- The division heads in a company which is spread out geographically discuss and agree on their respective responsibilities for a company proposal involving their separate operations.

- Several medical doctors representing differing specialities in one local area maintain a computerised consulting and referral network.

- Technical librarians in a group of non-competitive companies set up a document-exchange programme and jointly plan complementary acquisitions.

- Car service managers for one manufacturer maintain a conference concerning the merits and performance of test and maintenance equipment, or concerning unusual servicing problems.

- The manager of a decentralised development programme uses computerised conferencing to maintain contact with the group and monitor the status of various projects.

- A committee which meets regularly only once a month uses computerised conferencing to maintain continuous contact and to arrive at the agenda for its face-to-face sessions.

[1] Turoff 1974

- An author of a technical paper discusses it with a group of referees via an anonymous computerised conference.

- Members of legislatures caucus at will with a computerised conference.

- Policy-makers obtain quick response on the pros and cons of critical issues from experts scattered around the country.

The benefits of computer-conferencing are ones of travel time, convenience and value to the business. But there are disadvantages which could affect the results. Some individuals have regretted the absence of personal contact so important in delicate negotiations.[1] Others have found work at the terminal a tremendous energy drain, by being forced to concentrate harder than normal.[2] Other problems encountered are physical isolation, a reduced obligation to communicate, and the acceptance of a new set of human communication protocols and ethics.

Conference systems do exist now but are tending to be used only in situations where the economics and convenience of conventional meetings are grossly different to those of conferencing systems. The computerised conferencing systems are probably the most impersonal, and yet are those with the most potential, and are being used mostly in organisations with a high technical awareness (eg research establishments) and where computer terminals exist for other reasons.

Computer conferencing has a future as one of the functions of the electronic office. The first stage is probably limited to conferencing by private messages, avoiding the common forum, until awareness has grown and a new set of human communication protocols has developed.

## PRIVATE BRANCH EXCHANGES

The stored-program controlled telephone exchange has evolved over the past decade to provide a wide range of sophisticated voice handling facilities, data switching facilities and in addition environmental control facilities, such as building security and air conditioning control. More importantly each handset connected to a PBX can now be viewed as a powerful data terminal, through which data can be collected or enquiries can be made.

[1] Uhlig 1977
[2] Turoff 1977

These sophistications were initially available only on larger systems, but the Post Office has now placed an order for the production of a small microprocessor-controlled PBX with Pye TMC. This system called Herald will take up to 10 exchange lines and 30 extensions and will provide many of the facilities available on the larger IBM 3750 (350 exchange lines and 2500 extensions) and the Pye TMC EBX 8000 (850 exchange lines and 8000 extensions). Additionally the Post Office will be offering a system called Monarch 120, a digital microprocessor-controlled PBX, providing up to 120 extensions.

The major facilities available from stored-program-controlled private branch exchanges are listed below and show the flexibility that can be obtained:

- *Call redirection.* This allows users to divert all incoming calls to another extension. This ensures that calls will be routed automatically to the place where the user may be found.

- *Call pick-up.* This enables users to answer calls appearing on another extension.

- *Automatic call back.* This facility enables a user, on finding an extension engaged, to instruct the exchange to ring back and connect when both parties are free. (Sometimes called 'camp-on'.)

- *Multi-party conference calls.* This allows several users to be involved in the same conversation.

- *Abbreviated number dialling.* A library of regularly used external telephone numbers is maintained, and these can be obtained by keying 3 or 4 digits. Such abbreviated numbers can be maintained for company use or for use from individual extensions.

- *Call last number.* This enables the last number tried or connected to be re-tried by keying a short code.

- *Fast call connect.* A characteristic of stored programme PBXs is that internal calls are connected in less than 1 second compared with up to 15 seconds on electromechanical exchanges.

- *Manager/Secretary facilities.* These facilities can be provided between any extensions, without special wiring.

- *Moves and Changes.* Amendments to the system such as re-numbering extensions, and changes in class of service can be implemented without rewiring. The changes are made to the system usually by inputting them on a service terminal.

- *Route restriction.* This allows limits on external dialling and trunk dialling to be imposed selectively, dependent upon class of service of the extensions.

- *Route optimisation.* This allows the PBX to examine dialled numbers and to route the calls through lower-cost leased lines if these are free.

- *Direct night service to extensions.* This allows incoming calls to be made directly to selected extensions when the switchboard is unattended.

- *Call information logging.* This allows information on individual calls to be stored for either manual or computer analysis. This provides a basis for allocating telephone costs to user areas and for recharging individuals for the cost of private calls.

- *Traffic tables.* This allows various aspects of the traffic to be monitored, enabling figures on system performance and usage to be obtained.

- *Voice store and forward.* This facility is possible on digital exchanges although currently is only in use on an experimental basis. It enables digitised voice messages to be stored in the system for later delivery to or collection by the recipient.

The use of the handset as a data terminal has opened up numerous application possibilities for both data collection and data enquiry, with links to dp systems. Data collection applications include time-attendance recording, stock movement monitoring and ordering. Data enquiry applications include bank account status enquiries, and stock status enquiries.

The handsets being used as data terminals could be local extensions remote extensions (over leased lines) and from remote telephones over the PSTN. Responses to enquiries could take several forms. Tones can be returned in various predefined patterns in order to acknowledge receipt of data or to indicate a misunderstood message.

More information content can be communicated when an audio response is given. This could either be one of a set of prerecorded messages held in the PBX, or a synthesised voice message composed by the PBX or the dp system, giving commands or information to the user. The use of a handset as a data terminal extends the capability of a familiar device. In doing this, the PBX behaves as a terminal concentrator and terminal switching device and by using these facilities the PBX has the ability to act as a terminal concentrator or a message switching centre for the work-stations of an electronic office.

In its message switching capacity the PBX would enable work-stations to be placed by every phone in an organisation, using existing wiring, and it could link all the work-stations to each other and to central dp and printing facilities. In its terminal concentrator capacity the PBX could enable work-stations to be linked to both private and public networks and to public services. These could include the PSS (Packet Switched Services) network, Telex, Prestel, and the PSTN (Public Switched Telephone Network).

Sophistication of facilities need not be the exclusive right of those whose traffic warrants the installation of a PBX. The introduction of the Post Office's digital public telephone network (System X), scheduled for introduction in the mid-1980s, will see the use of stored-program exchanges which could offer many of the enhanced facilities, mentioned for PBXs, to each individual network user, both business and domestic.

## CHARACTER RECOGNITION

The automatic recognition of text and data from existing documents has been desired for a long time by many users but they have been hesitant to use existing products because of high rejection rates of unreadable characters. The equipment accepted mainly a limited range of special character fonts which meant that existing equipment had to be replaced or modified. More importantly it meant that the bulk of paper-based information that already existed and the majority of that flowing in from other organisations could not be read by the machines and would have to be re-keyed in order to enter computer systems.

Some of these problems are being eliminated by the use of micro-processors in character-recognition equipment. These developments have given units the ability to read conventional type-written copy and some can now cope with the following 'problem areas':

 - choice of type fonts;
 - 10- and 12-pitch type spacing;
 - free-format layout;
 - skewed or wavy lines;

- wrinkled, dog-eared, smudged copy (to a degree);
- typewritten insertions;
- single-spaced lines;
- underlining.

These enhancements mean that documents from a wider range of typewriters, and that a wider range of documents, can be used for input of information. However, unless people are conscious of the fact that a document is being prepared for reading by character recognition equipment, then problems can still occur. Mixed type faces, common on printed documents, and many special symbols and foreign language letters with accents and other diacritics will not be recognised.

Before the multi-font universal character set character reader is available, use can be made of today's products in the automated office environment. Restricting input to documents created in-house and to certain specifications, we can use existing typewriters for the creation of the first draft of a document. This document is then read onto a word processor for revision and correction. In this way an expensive word processor is used for the text manipulation process whilst the bulk of the straight typing can be done on existing standard typewriters. Additionally existing manuals and documents can be loaded onto a new word processing system without the need for re-keying where an appropriate type-font was used.

Vydec Inc offers a text reader, the Vydec Text Reader 761, for use with its word processor. This reader accepts only OCR-B and ECME 11 in type font and is useful for the situation where it is required to have 20 or 30 typewriters 'feeding' the word processor. The reader sells at £11,950 (1979 price). This price includes a diskette drive on which the interpreted text is output.

Newer developments are seen on the Hendrix Typereader 2 which offers microprocessor interfaces with a choice of 200 output programs to make it compatible with various word processors. Typed copy can be accepted in OCR-A, OCR-B and Hendrix Gothic, in 10- or 12-pitch spacing and single-spaced lines, and a wavy line can vary as much as half a character both up and down. The US price for this unit is $15,900 and it is marketed directly by many word processor suppliers.

The Dest Data Corporation's OCF/Wood unit can be made to accept any typewriter font that a customer cares to specify, although the basic unit is only equipped to recognise OCR-A, OCR-B, Courier 12 and 72 and Prestige Elite type styles. This machine is capable of accepting a wide range of intermixed weight of paper. The basic US price is $24,000.

Handprint readers are now accepting a wider range of characters. Previously restricted to numerics and several special symbols, alphabetics can now be catered for; for example, on the SCAN-DATA 2250 Data Entry System. The handprint readers being developed today are more tolerant of variations in character shape and size.

The freedom allowed for the input of handprint is still limited, with requirements for reference marks at the start of lines and boxes to regulate character positioning. Whilst these types of developments are making handprint recognition more sophisticated and eminently suitable in the formal business environment for data entry applications, such equipment is still far from being suitable for the free-form text input requirement of the electronic office.

Whilst the problems of handprint recognition are ones of recognising patterns which exist on paper, the problems of signature verification have been eased by an approach which examines the signature whilst it is being written. IBM's Research Division in New York has developed a signature-verification system which measures the pressure and the acceleration of the pen; this data is then compared with reference data. This is more reliable than a visual match of signature patterns and is giving 1.7% rejection of true signatures and 0.4% acceptance of deliberate forgeries.[1] This system will enable security systems to be developed which have a more natural interface and hence will be accepted by office automation users far more easily than a very impersonal password system.

The development of combined facsimile/optical character readers will create many opportunities for the manipulation of combined text and data. Stewart Warner[2] in the USA has developed a reader which will convert recognised characters to code and will digitise unrecognisable characters or other images; in this way combined text and images can be stored, transmitted and processed.

[1] Computer Weekly 5 Oct 78
[2] Anderson 1978

The Stewart Warner machine is estimated to be priced at $20,000 and is thought unlikely to be marketed in its current form. This type of technology has a place as part of the multifunction workstation in the electronic office. Muirhead in the UK are involved in experiments in joint OCR/facsimile and are likely to be the first to market such a device.

## PHOTOTYPESETTING

With the development of computer-based phototypesetting systems, organisations have an opportunity to generate in-house copy from which photographic plates can be produced. This shortens the tortuous iterations of typesetting, proof-reading, corrections and last-minute revisions often associated with outside contractors. With in-house phototypesetting, control of the work is retained until the last moment and lead times for final amendments can be shortened.

For much information, phototypesetting is the next stage after word processing. The use of high-quality print facilities associated with word processors (eg proportional spacing, even right hand margin and mixed fonts on dual daisy wheel printers) is reducing the proportion of work now needing to be typeset. Phototypesetters themselves do offer many of the text editing and storage facilities associated with word processors, in addition to the special printing commands. As a result, the phototypesetter is most commonly used as an independent unit where the original text is keyed, edited, corrected, and from which camera-ready copy is produced.

However, links between word processors and phototypesetters are becoming more common. For example, Itek have produced a microprocessor interface claimed to be capable of directly linking most word processors to their Quadritek phototypesetters, and Alphatype offer a plug-in facility to join their Alpha Comp phototypesetter to the Xerox 800 word processor. Other links are established by floppy disk or paper tape produced by a word processor being accepted by a phototypesetter.

The operation of the phototypesetter is in most cases still a very mechanical process. Images of the typefaces are on film on rotating disks or drums and the phototypesetter projects those images onto photosensitive paper, as dictated by the keyed text, to produce the camera-ready copy. Typically, at any one time a choice of four typefaces in a range of sizes would be available. These could all be mixed on one document.

With this type of technology the machines are typesetting at up to about 140,000 characters per hour (38 chars/sec). The typesetting speed is now being brought up to about 1 million characters per hour by the use of electronically generated images. In this situation the images are stored on magnetic disk and are then either generated on a CRT (cathode ray tube) and transferred by optic fibre to the paper (eg Linotype-Pauls 'Linotron 404'), or the character is described by a laser (eg Monotype-Laser Composer).

These types of systems do not have the mechanical limitations of the earlier phototypesetters and hence both speed and the number of typefaces available are vastly increased. At the moment the prices for the various types of systems are vastly different: £45,000 approximately (for the optic fibre or laser-based devices), rather than from £5,000 to £20,000 (for the earlier electro-mechanical phototypesetters).

Whilst there is always a need to produce prestige or high-volume printed work there will also be requirement for in-house phototypesetting. The increased use of word processors, which gives an opportunity for a direct input to a phototypesetter, and the falling costs of computer-driven equipment, will only serve as additional incentives.

## MICROFILM

In a world of magnetic storage of information there remains a desire to use an alternative storage mechanism, thereby creating some additional security. Microfilm is a physical means of storage. It is visible and the information can be seen to be present. Microfilm is currently at the end of a cul-de-sac: the techniques for microfilming computer-generated information are well tried and accepted. Computer-based indexing, cross-referencing and retrieval of microfilm is in use; for example, in the Mirror Newspaper Group's cutting room. But the input of microfilmed information to computer systems is in its infancy and not in wide use. The progress in this area is linked to progress in the character-recognition field. In due course, microfilm will be a useful storage medium for other information that needs to be reprocessed by computer systems.

Links between microfilm and other existing parts of office automation are becoming available. At the 1979 National Microfilm Association exhibition at Atlanta, Georgia, Planning Research Corporation announced their Telefiche System in which any

information on microfilm can be called up. The image is digitised
and then stored on disk or transmitted to be reconstituted either
on a VDU screen or by a facsimile device. This type of link opens
up new possibilities for microfilm; the refinement of character
recognition will make microfilm a flexible and secure storage
medium.

## PROPRIETARY OFFICE AUTOMATION SYSTEMS

The primary publicly available office automation system, or as
Tymshare Inc call it, an 'integrated office information system',
is the Stanford Research Institute system AUGMENT. This
system is now marketed by Tymshare Inc and is available as a
timesharing service either directly or through the TYMNET
value-added network. The system is currently only marketed in
the US and because of PTT regulations could only be available in
the UK as an intra-organisation system. This would deny the user
many of the wider benefits. A similar system (available in the UK,
developed by the National Physical Laboratory at Teddington, and
now marketed by Triad Computing Systems Limited) is called
Scrapbook, an 'Information Handling System'. Scrapbook is used
in the UK as an intra-organisation system.

## AUGMENT

The AUGMENT system, as marketed by the Augmentation
Resources Centre of Tymshare Inc, was initially developed in the
late 1960s as a system called NLS (On-Line System) at the Stanford
Research Institute, California. The funding for its development
was mostly from the US Department of Defence Advanced
Research Project Agency. NLS originally used the ARPANET
packet switched network as its principal means of communications.

The philosophy of NLS designer Douglas C Engelbart was that
each terminal should act as a person's total work-station providing
a complete 'knowledge workshop', and that by giving somebody
good tools the human intellect can be augmented, thereby increasing capabilities to an extent that would not be possible otherwise.

Because it was not feasible to extend the use of NLS to a much
broader base of commercial users whilst ARPANET alone was
being used, the rights of the system were purchased by Tymshare
in early 1978. NLS (then re-christened AUGMENT) was made
available to TYMNET users and as a timesharing service and
additionally make it available as an in-house service using DEC

system 20s (with or without network connection). In 1978 there were over 200 users of AUGMENT, mostly either defence or research organisations.

AUGMENT offers a full range of electronic office facilities including note taking, editing, revision, typesetting, collaborating, communicating, data base access, timesharing computer services, graphics facilities and mail box facilities. These facilities have been designed to be used by people with no data processing or technological training or experience. The system can be used from terminals with a wide variety of capabilities including simple portable typewriter terminals (eg Texas Instruments Silent 700) but if the facilities of the system want to be used with full efficiency then Tymshare recommend that the special AUGMENT 1200 terminal is used. A wide range of output devices can also be accommodated, including line printers and phototypesetters.

The AUGMENT 1200 visual display terminal is an intelligent device (Intel 8080 microprocessor-based) with a full keyboard, a cursor control device (the mouse) and a keyset (a 5-key chord keyboard). The full keyboard has a 'standard' typewriter layout with an additional row of command keys, although all commands can be issued from standard keys by the use of either full English words or mnemonics. 'The mouse' is a hand-sized plastic device with three buttons on the top and wheels beneath. Mouse movement on the desk controls the position of the cursor on the screen; the three buttons are used to issue a next obvious command, such as lock-the-cursor-onto-a-letter or acknowledge-an-action-of-the-system.

The keyset is used to generate characters by pressing combinations of keys. This 5-key keyboard is acknowledged to be difficult to learn; however, once mastered, the keyset and the mouse are the most efficient way to use the system. It is recommended that a new user should initially learn the command set and use of the mouse, before bothering about use of the keyset. The terminal display is buffered to hold 8,000 characters so that more information can be held locally than is displayed on the screen at any one time.

The facilities of AUGMENT are outlined below. In addition to these facilities, those who access AUGMENT through TYMNET or ARPANET also have at their disposal the computation, electronic mail and information base access facilities of those networks.

— *Text handling.* The text handling facilities offered include the now normal facilities of word processing systems such as insert, delete, search and replace and copy. But rather than organising a text file as a sequence of lines of text, AUGMENT allows reference to text in terms of its basic logical elements and organises them in levels which reflect their relationship. The basic logical elements of text are the ideas, be they sentences, paragraphs sections, diagrams or a row in a table. Each is a logical block of text and corresponds to the ideas expressed in the document.

AUGMENT does allow editing to be performed upon the intrinsic elements of text (words-phrases-lines) as does any other text editor, but the system references the basic building blocks of text and the hierarchical relationships between them as defined by the user. This structuring of text, eg chapter headings, sections, paragraphs and tables, simplifies the chapter and paragraph manipulation found to be cumbersome on most word processors.

— *Text browsing and retrieval.* The structure of the text files allows users to browse through documents at various levels as required. For example an initial browse can be at the top two levels, quickly dropping to a detailed level for a particular topic and returning to the top levels for the remainder of the document. This facility can be combined with more conventional pattern matching and logical retrieval functions.

— *Multiple displays.* Screens may be split into up to eight independent display areas. Each area of this screen may be independently controlled permitting concurrent viewing and manipulation of several files. Cross-file and multiple file editing and cross-referencing of documents are thereby easily facilitated.

— *Message handling.* Messages or documents may be sent to any number of recipients, in the same office or the other side of the country. They may be sent to individuals or to a preselected set of individuals. Delivery and notification take place within seconds.

— *Dialogue record.* This facility allows a common area between a group of users to be set up and used for permanently recording messages and documents that have been sent between members of that group. All items contained in the dialogue record may be retrieved any time by using the automatically generated keyword indices, accession numbers and catalogues. References to other on-line items may be included and this facilitates the automatic retrieval of related items.

The dialogue record provides for complete privacy or for public availability.

- *Linking of terminals.* Terminals can be linked so that everything that is viewed or printed at one terminal can appear simultaneously on another.

- *Graphics.* Text and line graphics can be mixed and used together in the same document, and with a high quality display terminal they may be viewed as they will appear in a final printed document.

- *On-line and off-line information entry.* Information may be entered directly from the terminal, or for more economic use of transmission line time, bulk information can be recorded on magnetic tape for later entry into the system.

- *Format facility.* A facility exists for creating and storing document formats and form layouts.

- *Spelling correction.* A 50,000-word dictionary exists which may be used to check the spelling of words in any document. Users can supplement the main dictionary with a personal dictionary.

- *Table manipulation.* Capability exists for entering organising, totalling and manipulating tables.

- *Sorting.* The facilities may be applied to documents lists and data.

- *Calculation.* Calculations can be specified and used on data being entered from the terminal or data in existence on files.

- *Privacy.* Access to every individual file may be limited by the owner of the file to individual users or groups of users. Information may additionally be encrypted. When files are shared, AUGMENT maintains a log of changes made to the files.

- *Security.* All files whether active or not are automatically copied and archived to provide protection against both hardware failures and accidental user errors.

- *User profile.* A profile of each user group or individual user is maintained, permitting user customisation of the system response. Details held include the level of prompting required and the nature of the command language to be used. This profile may be evolved as experience increases and requirements change.

— *On-line help.* This facility is designed for novice or infrequent users and provides either a breakdown of the things that may be done at any moment or it enters detailed question-answer sessions concerning the use of all AUGMENT facilities.

As a timesharing service AUGMENT provides firstly for the expansion of office automation in small capability and cost increments, and secondly provides organised housekeeping and operations support. The cost of using AUGMENT consists of several elements: there is a share of computing power, charges for information storage, computer network access charges, acquisition of work-station terminals and support services (training, consulting etc). Costs do depend on usage and are difficult to give but examples given in 1978 were, in addition to a $250 per month display terminal rental, anything from $11 to $22 per hour of system usage dependent upon file storage and the network charge rate applying to the area. This may seem expensive but typically an individual would use no more than two hours of time during a full working day.

## Scrapbook

Developed at the National Physical Laboratory, Teddington, and now marketed by TRIAD Computing Systems Limited, Scrapbook is an intra-organisation system offering document preparation, document distribution and personal information management facilities. Scrapbook is currently available on Computer Technology (CTL) 8000 series machines. Siemens' 7000 series machines and Digital Equipment PDP11 machines. Document files are stored centrally, and accessed via visual display unit terminals.

The system offers facilities for the drafting, editing and revising of documents and in addition to computer output printing it offers interfaces to phototypesetters. Each document on Scrapbook is identified by a document name which also defines hierarchical relationships between documents. System directories of documents are automatically maintained in lists which represent the document relations. A user may note other relationships in user directories. Directories may be accessed and browsed through either from the high-level system directory or up from the level of the document currently displayed.

Cross-references between and within documents may be included in text and be followed up conveniently as required. Examples of uses include citations from one document to another, structured documents where sections of text may be ignored if desired, and programmed instruction texts.

A user can send a message to a single recipient or to a predefined group of recipients. A message can be a line of text or a complete document. The presence of a message will, if possible, be notified immediately to the recipient or otherwise the system waits for the recipient to collect all messages.

Each registered Scrapbook user in an installation has a unique identity code with which he is referred to in the sending and receiving of messages and other identity purposes. Additionally he is allocated a password by the librarian; this password is used to gain access to the system. The librarian also maintains a 'permit document' for each user. The permit document specifies the type of actions that a user is allowed to perform on particular documents: for example, 'display only' or 'alter'. Documents can be classified as either 'public' or 'private'; where public a document can be read without specific permission, but permission is needed to alter it. A 'private' document requires a user to have permission before performing any operation upon it. Users of Scrapbook include the National Physical Laboratory, National Water Council and the Commission of the EEC in Luxembourg.

At the National Physical Laboratory, Scrapbook is used for the maintenance of frequently changing information such as stores catalogues or the configuration of the NPL network, project management, report writing, as an internal message system and for the registration of documents received at NPL.

At the National Water Council, Scrapbook has been used since May 1976. Installed on a CTL minicomputer, applications include the preparation of reports, the maintenance of a national water industry work-measurement information base and the preparation and distribution of a regular water industry bulletin utilising links to a Compugraphic phototypesetter and a Finn addressing machine. The introduction of Scrapbook into NWC was justified on the replacement of bureau services by in-house facilities.

The 1979 quoted cost for Scrapbook on CTL series 8000 with 8 terminals is £26,500 for the Scrapbook software licence and £56,200 for a CTL 8040, 8 terminals and 20 Mbyte of disk store.

AUGMENT and Scrapbook are office automation systems which are available now. AUGMENT, particularly, as a timesharing system, offers an easy way into the electronic office for the technologically-inexperienced user, with the subscription and usage fees covering every aspect of service and operational support.

Regulatory, rather than technical reasons, prevent the full facilities of the AUGMENT type of system being available in the UK. Despite this, both AUGMENT and Scrapbook, even as in-house systems, make ready-made electronic office facilities available today.

# 4 Hindrances and Challenges

Technological limitations to the development of the electronic office are minor by comparison to the challenges made by existing social, cultural and organisational attitudes. The technology for the fully integrated electronic office is here today; some of it may need refinement and some of it is expensive. Time and effort will solve these problems. The various hindrances and challenges will cause office automation to be introduced by evolution rather than by quantum leaps.

The rate of introduction of office automation will be dictated by its rate of acceptance at all levels of the business and social worlds. This includes the senior manager who must approve investment, the clerk who is concerned about changes in job content, and the teacher who has new basic skills to teach. The rate of acceptance will depend to a great extent on the level of awareness of office automation, its possibilities and its potential benefits. Even progress in alleviating the shortage of standards, which causes problems in communications and in the training of operators, depends upon users having an awareness of the need for standards.

## STANDARDS

A shortage of standards in the electronic-office area is likely to act as a major hindrance to its development for many years to come. Problems in communicating between machines, in interchanging media and in training of operators, are presented to users developing office automation systems. Standards are essential so that users can interwork without have to make prior exclusive arrangements. The interchange of media between different manufacturers' equipment needs standard specifications for the nature and use of the media. The retraining of operators to use different equipment currently wastes much time and effort because of variations in functions, commands and layouts.

In established areas of data processing many standards have been agreed and defined. However, because they are not followed by both users and manufacturers, the benefits of standardisation are not realised. In the electronic office three areas of interest meet; namely, office practice, communications and data processing. Each of these areas has its own traditions and practices and this has created a wide divergence in the nature of equipment available to the electronic office user.

The benefits of standards go far beyond helping the user to implement and operate. For instance, the open communication between text processors will create market opportunities likely to dwarf the current word processor market: when a user can buy a communicating text processor which can talk with most other users in the world, why would he ever want to buy a text processor that cannot communicate?

A new dimension will have been added to the capability of the text processor, useful both in document preparation and storage, and in information communication, through the single terminal having access to all other communicating text processors. In this situation the text processor may be considered in the same light as the business telephone today — hardly a desk being without one, with it accepted as the norm, and being installed without need for financial justification.

Questions concerning standards should be asked of the manufacturers at the procurement stage. The answers to these questions will show the manufacturers' awareness of the importance of standards and standardisation, and the likelihood of the manufacturers being prepared to modify software and interfaces to comply with future standards.

**Areas for Standardisation**

To illustrate some of the shortcomings in the standards world, a list of subject areas for standardisation relevant to the electronic office is given:

- Telecommunications:
    - terminal and device protocols;
    - file transfer protocols;
    - addressing of users;
    - error control;

- network independence.
- Interchange of media:
  - size, density;
  - data structures;
  - labelling.
- Operator interfaces:
  - keyboards:
    - shifts, function/editing keys, dead keys, layouts;
  - printers:
    - page formats, type fonts, proportional spacing;
    - paper handling.
  - displays:
    - formats, legibility, representation of characters;
    - emphasis.
  - operator controls;
  - text processing language.
- Data representation:
  - character sets, coding and contents;
  - control characters;
  - data elements, eg representation of dates:
    - times, abbreviations.
  - sort sequences;
  - encryption;
  - authentication.

In available products, there is a wide range of practices in each of the above areas; any standardisation activities are starting at a disadvantage, with various people backing a variety of the current practices. (Note: It may be a long time before standardisation is complete — if ever. This depends largely on the attitudes of suppliers and the demands placed upon them by users.) But standardisation in each of those areas above is important for the development of office automation. In this situation it seems that development will be slow.

## Overcoming the Shortage of Standards

The fact that there is a lack of standards does not mean that nothing can be done, but it does limit the possibilities. There are various methods of tackling the shortage.

### Restricted Purchase

By restricting purchase to a single model of equipment or to equipment which complies to certain specifications many of the problems of shortage of standards are overcome. This method applies within an organisation or within a community of interest where a rigid policy can be imposed. Problems can occur though when external *ad hoc* communication facilities are required.

### Restricted Operations

Although only possible to enforce within an organisation, the restriction of facilities can permit communication between super-ficially non-compatible devices. However, often the lowest common denominator which allows communications between unlike devices involves so many restrictions as to allow only a low level of sophistication. Problems with external *ad hoc* communications, training and media exchange can still occur.

### Restricted Access

A situation where access is limited to users of similar equipment can be beneficial if the equipment is popular. To be really useful a directory of such users is needed, so that although the number of users is restricted, *ad hoc* communications can be effected. Rank Xerox in the UK produces a directory of the users of their Tele-copier facsimile equipment thereby enabling *ad hoc* access to all listed Telecopier users; and, in the USA, Xerox offer a freephone enquiry service through which telephone numbers of other Tele-copier users may be retrieved.

### Customised Compatibility

The development of hardware and software to give compatibility between certain pieces of equipment can provide a limited solution to the shortage of standards. Microprocessor interface devices offered by suppliers to give their equipment compatibility with a wide range of other equipment are starting to be offered on the market. Again this will be only a partial answer to the shortage of standards, but perhaps the only practicable one for some time to come. There is a large existing population of terminals, many hard-wired. The 'black box' approach may be favoured as an expedient solution.

## Compatibility Services

Compatibility services are offered in the USA on value-added networks, and give communications compatibility between various makes of word processors and also between various makes of facsimile devices.

The degree of access to users is limited by the number of subscribers to the service on the network. Again, the facilities for use have to be restricted.

The ultimate method of overcoming a shortage is to generate the required standards. By their nature, standards necessitate a compromise in the requirements of various sections of interest and will therefore in themselves restrict facilities. However, the benefit of common working far outweighs any such disadvantages.

## De Facto Standards

Methods of working which become common in usage can become accepted as unofficial standards (eg IBM's EBCDIC character coding), or they can become adopted as official standards (eg IBM diskette specifications became ISO DP5464 and Philips cassette specifications were adopted for ISO 3407 and 3275).

## Enforced Standards

When communications services are provided, interface rules and equipment characteristics are specified. These have to be complied with before the service can be used, and in this way standard methods of working are enforced upon users and manufacturers. If the service offered is a public service then it is to the manufacturers' advantage to produce equipment which conforms. The proposed Teletex service (text communication service) under discussion in the CCITT will describe equipment characteristics and will offer a huge potential market for the manufacturers who wish to conform.

## Sectional Representation

Standards and recommendations are drawn up by bodies representing specific areas of interest. These organisations can often work faster than the national and international standards bodies with the result that their early recommendations are later adopted as official standards: even though not universally representative the recommendations are in wide use and often form the basis of important services. Such unrepresentative organisations are CCITT and ECMA (European Computer Manufacturers Association).

## Representative Agreement

Standards and recommendations can be drawn up by bodies in which all areas of interest can be represented; these exist nationally and internationally. Such bodies are ISO (International Organisation for Standardisation), BSI (British Standards Institution), and ANSI (American National Standards Institute).

## Existing Standards

In this section some of the existing standards relevant to the electronic office are listed. Some are data-processing based, some telecommunications-based and some office-equipment based. In the electronic office these three areas are coming together, and many products are available which have developed in one area alone and have ignored standards in the other two.

Whilst office equipment was completely self-contained, standards were of relevance from the safety and training point of view. Now that communications and media interchange is required, compliance to standards is of utmost importance to all users of office automation equipment. However, the existence of standards, however comprehensive, is not enough on its own; if users are not aware of the advantages, and manufacturers do not conform to them, then they may as well not exist.

In the list of standards the following abbreviations are used to indicate types of standards documents:

DC   a draft for comment (BSI) or 'draft'

DD   a draft for development — a pilot for an eventual British Standard and often produced to meet an urgent need.

DIS  a draft for international standard (ISO)

DP   a draft proposal (ISO) precedes a DIS in the standards-making procedure

PD   a published document. The published results of work which was thought useful but did not at the time become an official standard

R    recommendation.

## Data Representation

Letter symbols, signs and abbreviations
BS 1991 Part 1: 1976 General; Part 6: 1975
Electrical Science and engineering

The International System of Units (SI)
BS 3763: 1976

SI units and recommendations for the use of their multiples and of certain other units
BS 5555: 1976 and BS PD 5686; 1972 (ISO 1000)

Representation of elements of data in interchanges in data processing systems: The representation of dates and times
BS 5249: Part 1: 1976 (ISO 2711 and ISO 3307)

Representation of human sexes
BS 5249: Part 2: 1978 (ISO 5218)

Unit symbols for use in systems with limited character sets
BSI DD 8: 1971 (ISO 2955)

Representation of numeric values in character strings for information interchange
Draft BS 78/60711 (ISO/DIS 6093)

Representation of local time differentials
ISO 4031: 1978

Numbering of weeks
BS 4760: 1971 (ISO 2015)

Codes for the representation of names of countries
BS 5374: 1976 (ISO 3166)
Amended in 1977.

Codes for the representation of currencies and funds
Draft BS 76/63746 DC (ISO/DIS 4217)

Principles for abbreviation of titles of periodicals
BS 4148, Part 1: 1970

Word abbreviation list
BS 4148, Part 2: 1975 (ISO 833)

Abbreviations of typical words in bibliographical references
ISO 832: 1970

*Sorting*

Alphabetical arrangement and the filing order of numerics and symbols
BS 1749: 1969
Conforms with the sorting sequence for alphanumeric keys obtained naturally with the British Standard Data Code (BS 4730) but not that obtained with EBCDIC code.

*Safety*

Recommendations for safety of office machines and data processing equipment
BS 4644: 1970
Guidance for users as well as designers.

Electrical safety of office machines
BS 3861. Part 1: 1965; Part 2: 1968; Part 3: 1970
A revision of this comprehensive standard is given in Draft BS 76/61524 DC.

Codes of practice of fire protection for electronic data processing installations
Draft BS 78/60294 DC

*Character Codes*

The United Kingdom 7-bit data code
BS 4730: 1974 (ISO 646, ECMA-6, 4th Edition, CCITT R V.3 International Alphabet No. 5)
International Alphabet No. 2 (Telex) CCITT R F.1

Rules for the derivation of 4-bit coded character sets (from UK 7-bit data code)
BS 4731 Part 1: 1971 (ISO 963, ECMA-14)

Code extension techniques for use with the UK 7-bit data code
BS 4953: 1973 (ISO 2022, ECMA-35)

Procedure for registration of escape sequences
ISO 2375: 1974

Additional controls for character-imaging I/O devices
ECMA-48 (1976)

*Transliteration*

Transliteration of (Slavic) Cyrillic and Greek characters
BS 2979: 1958 (ISO 9 for Cyrillic, and ISO/DIS 843 for Greek)

Transliteration of alphabets of non-Slavic languages of the Soviet Union using Cyrillic characters
ISO/DIS 2805: 1975

Transliteration of Hebrew characters into Latin characters
ISO/DIS 259 (revision of 1975)

Transliteration of Arabic characters
BS 4280: 1968

Romanisation of Japanese
BS 4812: 1972

*Media Interchange*

3.81 mm magnetic tape in a cassette for data interchange — 31.5 b.p. mm. phase encoded
BS 5079: Part 1: 1974 (ECMA-34 2nd Edition ISO 3407 and 3275)

Data interchange on 3.81 mm magnetic tape cassette, dual track complementary return-to-bias four states recording
Draft BS 76/61912 DC (ISO 4339)

Data interchange on 6.3 mm magnetic tape cartridge 63 b.p. mm., phase encoded
ISO 4057: 1978 (ECMA-46)

Magnetic tape cassette labelling and file structure for information interchange
Draft BS 76/61733 DC (ISO 4341, ECMA-41)

Magnetic single-disk cartridge for data processing — (Top loaded) Part 1: Mechanical and magnetic properties
BS 5356: Part 1: 1976 (ISO 3562, ECMA-38)

Ditto — Part 2: track format
BS 5356: Part 2: 1976 (ISO 3563, ECMA-39)

200 mm flexible disk cartridge recorded at 13262 ftprad on one side — mechanical and magnetic properties
ISO/DP 5654: Part 1: 1977 (ECMA-54)

Ditto — track format
ISO/DIS 5654: Part 2: 1978 (ECMA-54)

*Stationery*

Sizes of papers and boards
BS 4000: 1968 (ISO 216)

Sizes and recommended layout of commercial forms — letterheads and forms
BS 1808 Part 1: 1970 (ISO 216)

Ditto — continuous stationery (for general office use)
BS 1808: Part 2: 1967

Personal stationery (terms and sizes)
BS 1360: 1973 (ISO/R 353)

Line spacings and character spacings on office machines and data processing equipment
Draft BS 77/63441 DC (ISO 4882)

Office machines — line and character capacity of address masters
BS 5560: 1978 (ISO 3883)

*Keyboard and Office Equipment*

Typewriters
BS 2481: 1975

Basic arrangements for the alphanumeric section of keyboards operated with both hands
ISO 2126: 1975

Layout of printing and function keys on typewriters
ISO 1091: 1977

Function key symbols on typewriters
ISO 1090: 1969

Keyboards generating the code combinations of the characters of the ECMA 7-bit coded character set
ECMA-23 Second Edition (1975)

Keyboard arrangements for data processing — the graphic characters of the UK 7-bit data code
BS 4822: Part 1: 1972 (ISO 2530)

Keyboards for countries whose languages have alphabetic extenders — Guidelines for harmonization
ISO 3243: 1975

Principles governing the positioning of control keys on keyboards of office machines and data processing equipment
BSI 5231: 1975 (ISO 3244)

Modification of keyboards to include symbols for SI units (international system)
BSI PD 6462: 1972

Keyboard layouts for numeric applications on office machines and data processing equipment
BS 5448: 1977 (ISO 3791)

Ribbons and spools used on office machines and data processing equipment
BS 5519: Part 1: 1977 (ISO 2258)
BS 5519: Part 2: 1977 (ISO 2257)
BS 5519: Part 3: 1977 (ISO 2775)
BS 5519: Part 4: 1977 (ISO 3540)
BS 5519: Part 5: 1977 (ISO 3866)

*Ergonomics*

Anthropometric recommendations for dimensions of office machine operators' chairs and desks
BS 3404: 1961 (Also BS 3044 and 3079)

Office desks, tables and seating
BS 3893: 1965

Chair-desk working position — Basic principles
Draft BS 77/63781 DC

Ditto — Dimensions and design requirements
Draft BS 77/63782 DC

*Optical Character Recognition*

Optical character recognition — Character set OCR-A.
Shapes and dimensions of the printed image
BS 5464: Part 1: 1977 (ISO 1073: Part 1, ECMA-8). This is a highly stylised font of numerals and four special symbols.

Ditto — Character set OCR-B. Shapes and dimensions of the printed image
BS 5464: Part 2: 1977 (ISO 1073: Part 2, ECMA-11, 3rd Edition)
A complete alphanumeric font with both capital and small letters. OCR-B is available on normal typewriters.

OCR-B subsets for numeric applications
ECMA-30 Second Edition (1976)

Alphanumeric character set for 7 x 9 matrix printers
ECMA-42 (1973)

Implementation of the numeric OCR-A font with 9 x 9 matrix printers
ECMA-51 (1977)

Printing specifications for optical character recognition
ISO 1831: 1978 (ECMA-15)

Recommended OCR paper specifications
ECMA unnumbered document, second edition 1977

Recommended sizes of forms for optical reading
ECMA white cover document, 1972

Printing line position on single line documents
ECMA-18 (1968)

Character positioning on OCR journal tape
ECMA-21 (1969)

*Microfilm (COM) and Microfiche*

Quality requirements for computer output on microfilm
BSI/DD 27: 1973

Transparent A6 size microfiche of uniform division – Image
arrangement No. 1 and 2
BS 4187: Parts 1 and 2: 1973 (ISO 2707)

Ditto – Formats of 208, 325 and 420 frames
Draft BS 77/63311 DC

Transparent A6 size microfiche of variable division – Image
arrangements A and B
ISO 2708: 1976

Transparent A6 size microfiche – Additional physical characteristics
ISO/DIS 3273: 1973

High reduction microfiche
Draft BS 75/63270

Recommendations for preparation of copy for microfilming
BS 5444: 1977

Computer output microfiche
Draft BS 76/60316

Specification for microform readers
BS 4191: 1976

*Data Transmission*

Standards in this area and their significance are covered more
fully in *Introducing Data Communications Standards,* Scott
P.R.D., NCC Publications, 1979.

- Digital Data Transmission

  BS 4505 Part 1-7
- High level data link control procedures

  BS 5397

  ISO DIS 4335

  ISO DIS 6159

  ISO DIS 6256
- List of definitions for interchange circuits between data terminal equipment and data circuit terminating equipment

  CCITT R V.24

  Allows two pieces of computer-like equipment to be connected together.
- Interface between DTE and DCE for terminals operating in the packet mode on public data networks.

  CCITT R X.25

  Defines the connections of terminals to packet switched data networks.

*Facsimile*

Facsimile apparatus capable of transmitting an A4 size document in 6 minutes (Group 1 facsimile apparatus) CCITT RT2

Facsimile apparatus capable of transmitting an A4 size document in 3 minutes (Group 2 facsimile apparatus) CCITT RT3

Facsimile apparatus capable of transmitting an A4 size document in nominally 1 minute using redundancy reduction techniques (Group 3 facsimile apparatus) Provisionally CCITT RT4 due for ratification at the CCITT Plenary session in Autumn 1980.

**Standards-Making Bodies**

**BSI (British Standards Institution).** The national standards-making body in the UK, BSI, takes into account the views of users and manufacturers. Data processing and office equipment are two of the many areas of interest covered by BSI Standards.

**ISO (International Organisation for Standardisation)** aims to set up international standards and to facilitate the coordination of national standards.

IEC (International Electrotechnical Committee) is interested in safety and standardisation aspects of electrical equipment.

CCITT (International Telegraph and Telephone Consultative Committee) coordinates and represents the interests of national telecommunications administrations. Amongst its many functions it develops and specifies standards for the design and operation of telecommunications services.

ANSI (American National Standards Institute) often leads in the production of computer language standards.

ECMA (European Computer Manufacturers Association) has been the source of many effective standards subsequently adopted by ISO.

Advice on existing standards and on current standards-making activities is available free from the Standardisation Office, NCC.

## PERSONNEL CONSIDERATIONS

### Quality of Working Life

The introduction of new technology into the office will bring with it many changes and there will be a natural resistance to those changes. Labour displacement (either by redundancy or natural wastage) is unfortunately the typical justification for introduction of office automation equipment, and changes in employment prospects must be the worst change for individuals to face. Other changes too will receive stiff opposition. There will be changes in job structures and in traditional working relationships. Old hard-learnt skills will lose value and new skills will be necessary. Certain individuals will have reduced responsibilities whilst others will take on more. These changes present challenges to both management and worker concerning their implementation. Whilst accepting the challenge and attempting to smooth these changes the opportunity for improving the quality of work must not be ignored.

In this section many of the problems and opportunities discussed will be found to relate more to the clerical area than to the managerial and professional area. Even though it is support of the latter which is the long-term aim of office automation, for today and the near future, concern will be with the implementation in the clerical area.

The opportunities presented fall into the categories of:

- job enlargement;
- job rotation;
- job enrichment;
- semi-autonomous workgroup.

## Job Enlargement

Instead of having a part of some task to complete, the individual is given responsibility for some reasonably complete task; for instance, taking a report from draft to phototypesetting, instead of just typing the report. The job enlargement could simply be more tasks of the same type (for example, all typing operations) or it could be that other elements are included (for example, the security copying of word-processing diskette files).

One concern is that office automation will lead to de-skilling and machine-minding. While the nature of the operation or process may make this inevitable, eg printer control in shared-resource word processing, it does not mean that some responsibility cannot be attached to the job. Enlargement may restore a task to an adequate level for a reasonable amount of job satisfaction.

Given that microelectronics provide a cheap control capacity, it means that any one individual will be able to have a wider span of control over a given process, eg one operator controlling several optical character readers. There should therefore be a tendency towards job enlargement, affecting management as well as clerical staff; for example, when Citibank in New York introduced a management work-station system and one of the objectives was to increase the span of control of their line managers from an average of 7 to 9.

## Job Rotation

The introduction of automated equipment can mean that much physical activity is eliminated. Instead there may be longer periods of inactivity but a greater need for perceptual and monitoring skills. A degree of social isolation may be introduced as the number of people needed to perform a task is reduced, eg reduced staffing of a computer-controlled PBX. To minimise this sort of problem, some form of job rotation can be introduced. As with job enlargement, this does require a degree of flexibility of the operators. Social isolation for managers and technical workers could become a severe problem as electronic communications reduces the incidence of personal contact. Job rotation in the strict sense would be difficult to apply to such employees and maybe some more radical approach, eg mandatory communal lunches, may need to be taken.

## Job Enrichment

With the control capabilities of microelectronics it will be possible for the operator to assume a greater degree of responsibility for the quality of the output. This could be important as the through-put is increased because of the greater sophistication of equipment. Since a good deal of frustration can be generated if the operator is not able to make decisions relating to the method of working it is sometimes useful to introduce a degree of enrichment to a job.

This means that instead of just enlarging the job horizontally, it is enlarged vertically, and the operator assumes some of the responsibilities usually associated with the supervisor. This can include such things as quality control, liaison with other sections, scheduling of their own work, and ability to stop the work if it is thought there is something wrong. Again the control capabilities of microelectronics should mean that it is easier to introduce such job enrichment. An example would be the possibility of the secretary becoming an entry-level management job. A vital task in this area is the identification of tasks the supervisor or manager can take on to replace those elements lost because they have been devolved to subordinates.

## Semi-Autonomous Work Group

Even though the relationship between operator and supervisor may be changed by a job-enrichment programme, the basic hierar-chical structure remains. In certain circumstances, a job redesign exercise may alter even this relationship. Once the operators have been adequately trained in some group of tasks, and have ex-perience working with other sections and departments the super-visor may withdraw completely and leave the group to manage itself.

The people in the group then assume responsibility for meeting targets, scheduling the work and rest periods, and decide between themselves the job content and frequency of rotation. There are very few examples where this has been attempted in a manu-facturing environment, but such semi-autonomous group working may be more appropriate in clerical areas. The extensive nature of the changes means that it is often only when a company is in a 'greenfield site' situation that it considers such a scheme. Even then it requires operators of a high standard, and they require a good deal of training to achieve sufficient flexibility and to establish good working relationships within the group.

The four areas of opportunity for improving the quality of working life as outlined above do not provide a means of avoiding the problems. The changes have to be implemented and challenges are thrown up in three main areas:

— job content;

— involvement;

— pay and promotion.

## Job Content

De-skilling as a result of introducing new technology is obviously a possibility, but to maintain the necessary level of interest and motiviation an organisation can add additional elements to a job. This could cut the number of staff elsewhere, eg indirect clerical staff if an operator should assume some responsibility for inputting information into the system, but it would mean a more responsible and more varied job for the operator.

Traditional typist training has had the objective of teaching the production of good copy at the first go, and teaching good letter and report layout. Word processors are tending to devalue these skills. Corrections can be made using minimum effort before the work is committed to paper. House styles for letters can be defined as a standard format within which word-processor operators work. The use of dictation systems is lowering the value of shorthand, in favour of audio typing skills. Keyboarding skills are not possessed by large sections of office staff but as automation facilities proliferate then requirements for these skills will become widespread at all levels in the organisation. Managers may show resistance to the ideas of using a keyboard themselves and some will always require an interface between themselves and technology.

In traditional office culture the secretary does all the typing and filing and the manager does none, and this can create the feeling that for a manager to learn a keyboard skill is demeaning. This type of cultural attitude will change gradually as a new generation of managers, who have these basic skills and who have an awareness of office automation, come into the ranks.

The provision of calculator facilities and spelling aids on work-stations contribute to the devaluation of two traditional hard taught skills (mental arithmetic and spelling). Spelling ability is traditionally held in high regard and this has created a reluctance on the part of individuals to admit the need for automatic spelling aids.

Whatever the nature of the changes in a job redesign project there is almost inevitably greater flexibility for the staff involved. The re-examination of the basic tasks that are necessary and the redistribution of those tasks mean that operators can make more effective use of their time. If the changes introduced by new technology allow even a small increase in the operator's span of control then it should mean fewer operators will be needed to perform the same amount of work. And if there is an increase in the vertical span of control then there could be less direct supervision, and fewer levels of supervision. On the other hand the number of indirect staff developing the new technology system, and the number of people within the organisation involved in training and retraining could increase.

One trend which could develop as a consequence of new technology is the compression of the production and clerical processes. Certain tasks could be eliminated; for instance, an on-line clerical system could do away with the need for elaborate systems of coordinating paperwork.

## Involvement

One barrier to job-design exercises is the existing custom and practice. People are likely to resist changes unless they understand the reasons for change, and unless there is some obvious incentive for them to change. On the question of involvement it is possible to distinguish two levels, the national and the local.

At the national level there are going to be increasing demands by unions to be involved when the introduction of new technology is being considered. This will be both to show existing members that they are concerned about the potential job loss, and also to encourage new members who might be apprehensive about the implications for their current job.

The unions are likely to be concerned not just about increasing their membership but also changing the profile of membership. For example, if new technology is the greatest threat to the unskilled and semi-skilled then unions could try and establish a power base among the skilled technical and supervisory sections. Alternatively they could attempt to consolidate their position among the unskilled and semi-skilled to strengthen their bargaining position. Which approach they adopt could have implications for job design because of the issue of regrading. If an operator is upgraded, or if the operator takes some of the work of the supervisor, then agreement will be easier to reach if there is no union involvement, or if there is just one union involved, than if the change has to be acceptable to two or more unions.

At the local level the case for introducing changes will depend largely on the nature of the relationship established between management and unions. If the changes are not going to involve large-scale redundancies things should be easier. In a good many job-design projects there is a 'no redundancy clause' so that any spare capacity in numbers of people is coped with through relocation within the company and by natural wastage. Many of the issues that develop in job design, and possibly also with new technology, will be such that they can only be dealt with at the local level. For instance individuals will vary in the amount of variety and responsibility they want from a job. They may also resist the change and prefer to work in the established manner until they can see how other people are affected by the changes. Only later may they be willing to go over to the new methods of working. Issues like this ought to be agreed at the local level. The more the staff are involved in the detailed planning of how their jobs will change as a result of office automation the less likely it is there will be resistance at the implementation phase.

Key workers can be identified and involved early. Pilot projects and experiments should be established, letting the experiences of those involved be shared with other workers, thus helping to increase general awareness. Each area should be seen to be studied separately, with implementations planned to suit the local situation. Cultures do vary across organisations and no one-off implementation for an organisation will meet the requirements of all the existing cultures and traditions. Changes can be introduced gradually, avoiding the 'at a stroke' approach; staff are being stretched enough in being asked to accept changes without imposing them overnight.

## Pay and Promotion

One of the major concerns of individuals and of unions is the number of jobs. Even with a no-redundancy agreement there could still be a loss of jobs through natural wastage. In an attempt to minimise problems, organisations could well stop recruiting, and, if so, the group likely to be most affected will be the school leavers. The need for these measures could have a long-term effect in that the organisation will have to work with current resources. This could mean that some large-scale retraining may be necessary.

The thought of fewer jobs being required because of office automation is no happy prospect. But to remain competitive in a world market the opportunities for extra efficiency and productivity afforded by the electronic office cannot be ignored. Without adoption of more productive techniques there could be the prospect of even fewer jobs in the future as organisations stagnate and become uncompetitive. However, by taking the opportunities offered them, the possibility exists for increased output to maintain employment levels.

Within existing cultures, reconciling the idea of fewer jobs against increased competitiveness is not easy. Does the work ethic need revision? Tim Webb of ASTMS, the white collar union, has said[1] "We must develop an entirely new attitude toward working; the social stigma of redundancy and unemployment must be removed. People should expect to change the course of their careers five or six times in a lifetime."

With the possibility of fewer people needed for the same amount of production there could also be problems with promotion prospects. This should not be a problem for people with skills that are in short supply, eg personal secretaries, as they will be able to improve their position by moving jobs. It could be a problem for those with less-developed skills. This issue has come up with the introduction of semi-autonomous workgroups where the removal of a level of supervision has meant fewer prospects for those in the group. This has sometimes been overcome by upgrading all those in the group so they come somewhere between the operator and supervisor pay levels.

As with other job-design changes, new technology is bound to raise problems with regard to job-evaluation systems. Jobs may be altered in their content and there could be a wider variety of elements included within the job. Or there could be a merging of different jobs; for example, when an operator does some preventative maintenance.

Those involved in maintenance may have to acquire skills which would align them to some extent with other grades, and as technical skills become even more important there may have to be

[1] Computing 10.8.78

changes in the weighting of man-management and technical skills in the evaluation of jobs. The existing job-evaluation scheme may be inadequate in the face of all these demands; modified or new evaluation schemes may need to be introduced.

The monitoring capabilities of microprocessors also mean that there could be changes in the type of payment system. This capability means that it will be much easier to link various forms of bonus payment with the total quantity or quality of output. This could be in some form of added-value scheme or it could be linked to the individual operator. For example the number of keystrokes of a word processing operator can be measured very accurately. Since however there is not necessarily a direct correlation between level of activity and efficiency, companies may prefer to remain at a more global level when it comes to incentive payment schemes. Although on-line work measurement may at first sight appear to provide the basis for an equable reward system, the concept of automatic monitoring is not popular. In West Germany such action is banned and is resisted by clerical unions in the UK.[1]

The development of a personnel programme for office systems, consistent with the system's design and the organisation's overall personnel policy, is an important part of an office automation implementation plan. The selection and placement of office personnel to support management at all levels requires a well structured plan. Personal characteristics, skills, knowledge and experience should be matched as closely as possible to the identifiable needs of the principals, and the complexity and value of the work. A mismatch will reduce management acceptance of systems and reduce the motivation of office personnel.

The following should be appreciated whenever people are matched to office system jobs:

— the needs of the principal;

— the qualities required to meet those needs;

— the value of the work to the organisation.

A systematic approach to the development of a personnel plan will provide the understanding of the above, and should include the following activities:

[1] Apex 1979

- job analysis;
- job description;
- job evaluation;
- career development programme.

These are discussed at greater length in Chapter 5.

## INVESTMENT IN OFFICE ACTIVITIES

Within industry it is traditional to view the office as a non-productive unit and as a unit whose running costs must be kept as low as possible. The factory on the other hand produces hard saleable goods, goods which have a direct impact on the bottom line of the profit and loss statement. Accordingly investment in the factory process is accepted as the norm.

Information, now a prime material to be used in the production of saleable products, should stand with equal importance alongside land, labour and capital. An increase in the accuracy and timeliness of information on which decisions are based can impact the effectiveness of the whole organisation. Likewise, increases in speed of communications and the increased personal support can lead to increased productivity of individuals.

Unfortunately, traditional practice does not encourage support of this type of activity. Office investment is based on cost-saving exercises, ie exercises which either reduce the cost of producing the same output or increase the throughput whilst only employing the same people. It is a neat approach. The cost savings can be clearly demonstrated and all intangibles ignored. The only substantial cost saving to be made in the office environment is the reduction in the wages bill, with the other side of the equation being the introduction of the minimum amount of technology required. Labour displacement is measurable making the benefits quantifiable, thereby conforming to traditional corporate investment attitudes.

Improvements in information provision and personal support do not exhibit easily quantifiable benefits, and even the most enlightened investment manager would have reason to question the values attributed to the benefits. Some of the problems being met are the measuring of the value of a manager's time and the quantifying of the worth of the decision-making ability. Even when there is an unquestionable benefit there is a problem in valuing that benefit so that investment in equipment can be justified.

Some organisations have automated these added-value activities. The ways of introducing them have varied, but rarely have values attributed to the benefits been the major reason for automation. Such activities have been automated as a by-product of cost-saving exercises. Examples of this are mainframe-based text-processing systems being introduced on the basis of a reduced head-count and then being additionally used for personal filing and message communication.

A competitive environment may also encourage automation of activities. For example, several chemical companies now use word processors for drug documentation. Of these, ICI Pharmaceuticals Division use Vydec word processors in the preparation of drug registration documentation and by doing so have substantially reduced the elapsed time required for the preparation of drug submissions and hence the time taken for drugs to be available on the market. The use of word processing techniques eases the preparation of the initial documentation and subsequently permits submissions to be tailored to the requirements of each of the national regulatory authorities without engaging in a vast re-typing exercise. A Vydec-to-Vydec link has been established between ICI Pharmaceuticals Alderley Park and its American counterpart. One objective of this link is to speed up some of the management decision processes involved in the drug sub-mission activity, with the possibility of further reducing the elapsed time. This type of activity will give a commercial advant-age which others in the market will have to counter.

Innovative organisations will take steps into this area by indulg-ing in experimentation. This type of organisation is aware of the potential and is prepared to commit funds to trial use of the equipment, monitoring the results, the benefits, and the affects on the organisation.

Experimentation and collaboration with other bodies allow the benefits of added-value activities to be appreciated. Familiarity and awareness can grow and there is an opportunity to iron out some of the problem areas in a controlled environment. Currently the equipment is expensive, but the costs are dropping, and if full advantage is to be taken of the time when costs are low then experience should be gained early. Experimentation can provide that experience. Innovative organisations will learn the lessons early, whilst the followers will apply those lessons, but always several steps behind.

Much office equipment in use today cannot be justified on

utilisation rate. However, in many organisations availability of the equipment is accepted as normal practice.

The following figures for utilisation of office equipment are quoted by IBM:

- Telephone:              14%;
- Copier:                 10%;
- Typewriter:             20%;
- Dictation Equipment:    13%;
- Calculators:            1%;
- Telex:                  10%.

The telephone is only utilised 14% of the time but is considered to be an integral part of the modern office. On a cost-justification basis many telephones would not be installed, but the benefits, although not costed, are so widely accepted and understood that the telephone is now part of office life.

The equipment of the electronic office is not yet accepted to that extent. Its benefits are not yet fully appreciated, and its price is still such that there can be no installations without cost benefits being clearly demonstrated. Office automation has yet to prove itself, the concepts and the technology are young, and there are many pitfalls. Until there is general acceptance and awareness from all levels of staff then each application must expect to be fully justified.

## ERGONOMIC FACTORS

Ergonomic considerations are important not only from the point of view of convenience, comfort and safety of the operators but also for the need to minimize errors caused by bad human interfaces. These problems are compounded by the fact that, as equipment becomes more powerful and as operators assume more responsibility, the consequence of undetected errors also increases.

Human interface aspects of work-station and systems design are becoming more important. Junior staff may have worked for years with badly-designed equipment, have made plenty of errors and have been thoroughly unhappy, but now that clerical staff are becoming more unionised, unions are taking a healthy interest in ergonomic problems.

A second factor which may influence the demise of poorly

designed equipment is the increasing use of office equipment by managers who, although less unionised than junior staff, have more powerful individual voices when complaining about systems. It is likely that many managers would let the system fall into disuse rather than struggle along with a bad design. This is bad for individual performance possibilities and for the organisation as a whole.

Complaints about mental and physical fatigue brought on through using office equipment are very difficult to quantify, but various factors are known to cause or aggravate fatigue. Attention to these can overcome the majority of problems. The following are considered:

- visual factors;
- postural factors;
- personal factors;
- environmental factors;
- task requirement factors;
- nature of system factors.

**Visual Factors**

Visual display units, keyboards and source documents cause visual and general fatigue.

*Displayed Image Factors (See Figure 13)*

- *Size of characters on vdu screens.* Characters should be at least 3mm high and result in a minimum viewing angle of 20' for normal viewing distance.[1]
- *Shape of characters on vdu screens.* The characters are commonly produced digitally from a dot matrix pattern. The 5 by 7 dot matrix produces characters which are only just acceptable if properly designed. The stroke width should be between 1/8 and 1/6 of character height and the character width should be between 70% and 80% of character height. Lower case descenders should go below the line.[1]
- *Spacing of characters.* The horizontal spacing should be between 20% and 50% of character height. Line spacing should be between 50% and 150% of character height.[1]

[1] Stewart 1978(I)

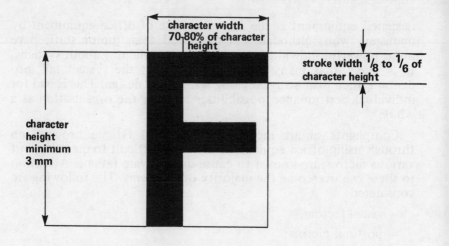

**(a)    Size and shape of characters**

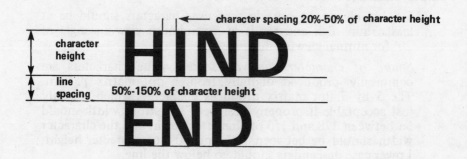

**(b)    Spacing of characters**

**Figure 13    Characters on Vdu Screens**

- *Resolution of characters.* The screen should be adjusted so that the characters are sharply defined and in focus. The capability to achieve high resolution will change over a period of time (say two years) with changes in the condition of the phosphorus coating the screen.

- *Stability of characters.* Flickering of the characters is caused by a low refresh rate. The refresh rate should be at least 50Hz. Other problem areas are character movement and variations in intensity.

- *Contrast.* The characters should stand out clearly from the background and not be obscured by excessive illumination or reflections.

- *Luminance.* Excessive luminance ratios between the screen and the rest of the environment and between the characters and the rest of the screen should be avoided. On a totally black screen the characters appear to float and make it difficult for the eye to accommodate properly.

In most installations the effective size of the characters is likely to be adequate, provided that other factors have not degraded legibility too much. As the characters have to be viewed at a finite distance, accommodation will be required. This may present no problem to the younger operator, but for the older person is likely to have to be at their normal reading distance. For operators wearing bifocals the vdu will need to be within the limits of a bifocal correction.

In addition to accommodation, the eyes will need to converge onto similar areas of a display to supply single unconfused imagery to the brain. Convergence fatigue commonly causes more problems than difficulty with accommodation, particularly at unaccustomed distances and positions and where short periods of relaxed distance gaze are not possible.

*Keyboard Factors*

- *Reflections from the keyboard.* The shape and texture of the key surface can minimise the problem.

- *Illegible key legends.* This can be another source of difficult images.

- *Fixed keyboards.* These can cause difficulties if the viewing distance is different from the screen and document.

*Source Document Factors*

- *Illegible documents*. These become even more difficult to read when used as source documents for a visual display unit.

- *Excessive illumination.* Over-illuminated source documents pose difficult adaptation problems for the eye moving between document and screen.

- *Document holders.* Inadequate (or lack of) document holder can result in an accommodation problem for the eye with viewing distances different for keyboard, screen and document.

**Postural Factors**

Posture factors can cause a general fatigue, and visual fatigue may be an early symptom of this.

- *Awkward posture.* Awkward postures may be adopted to compensate for bad work-station design, visual factors and unadjustable furniture.

- *Fixed posture.* Lack of movement is generally fatiguing, and this can be exacerbated by fixed keyboards. More generally, the increasingly sophisticated communication and control facilities offered by office automation will reduce the need for physical movement. The effect of decreased mobility on mental and physical well-being could be detrimental both personally and organisationally.

**Personal Factors**

These may result in greater susceptibility to fatigue.

- *Uncorrected visual defects.* Previously tolerable defects may be not acceptable when working with a vdu. It has been suggested[1] that even though conventional eye tests, carried out under static viewing conditions, may indicate normality, viewing difficulties may arise under the dynamic vision conditions of the vdu, keyboard, document environment.

- *Constitution.* Age, health, obesity, smoking and drink factors can all contribute to fatigue in all work environments.

[1] Bedwell C.H. 1978

## Environmental Factors

- *Lighting.* Inadequate or excessive lighting levels, uneven distribution of light, and glare from vdu screens and trims can aggravate fatigue.
- *Heat, humidity and condition of air.* Overheated and dry offices, with smoky atmospheres, contribute to general fatigue.
- *Noise.* Noise both from within the work area, eg fans and printers, or from outside, eg traffic, aircraft and adjacent work areas, can be distracting and reduce individual performance.
- *Territory.* Office design and the need to interact, balanced against the need for personalisation and privacy, are important considerations.

## Work Design Factors

The pace of work, the concentration required, the time spans of involvement with each task and the rest periods will all either improve or compound the situation.

## Nature of Systems

Office systems should fit into the office environment, using office language and procedures rather than those of data processing and of the computing world whence the equipment came. The operator/system interfaces need to be simple and feel natural to use, and the systems need a degree of flexibility to enable them to match the requirements of the various work areas in which they are applied.

Initially, users judge office systems on availability for use, and only later, when a degree of familiarity has been established, are deeper criticisms made. It is at this stage that the systems require that degree of flexibility so that they can evolve with the users' requirements.

Attention paid to the above ergonomic factors will avoid the majority of problems of fatigue and frustration which can lead to reduced individual and group performance.

In summary the important points are:

- a clear stable vdu image;
- adequate but not excessive illumination on keyboard and source documents;

- positioning vdu screens to avoid reflection from windows and other sources;

- correctly-positioned work-surfaces with easy-to-use document holders;

- easily adjustable chairs;

- work designed considering the need for rest periods and movement;

- selection of equipment considering the office culture, simplicity and flexibility.

## Radiation From VDU Screens

The increased use of vdus in graphics, word processing and data handling applications has led to some worries concerning the danger of radiation from vdus. It is now generally accepted that there is no danger.

In 1977 a survey was conducted by the US National Institute for Occupational Safety and Health (NIOSH)[1] in which electro-magnetic radiation was measured for several models and types of video display terminals. The values obtained for x-ray, ultraviolet, visible infra-red, and radio-frequency radiation were well below the considered safety levels. The question though has been asked[2] as to the possibilities of faulty units producing radiation which could be damaging to the long-term user. If this possibility does exist, then the use of monitoring equipment may be necessary.

## Induction of Epileptic Fits

About half a percent of the population suffers from epilepsy and about 4% of these are liable to seizures induced by visual stimulation.[3] In a substantial proportion of visually-sensitive patients, fits can be induced by striped patterns. A conventional domestic television or vdu can readily induce fits in most of those patients.

The epileptogenic properties of a television or a vdu can be reduced by:

- reducing the area of retina stimulated. By using small screens, light characters on a dark background and by limiting the amount of text presented at one time;

[1] Moss C.E. et al Dec 1977
[2] Apex Mar 1979
[3] Wilkins Dec 1978

- eliminating scrolling text;
- reducing the mean luminance of the display. By wearing dark glasses or by using a darkened perspex cover on the screen.

The epileptogenic properties of vdus do present a problem to a small proportion of the community. The problem has to be kept in perspective, but is worth considering when known epileptics are likely to be asked to use a vdu.

## NATURE OF SYSTEMS

The way in which systems show themselves to users and the capacity of them to evolve with users' requirements will be an important factor in the success of electronic office systems.

In traditional data processing there are usually several levels of interface in the operation of a system. Each user follows rigid procedures having undergone strict job training. However in office automation systems we are seeking not to perform specific tasks but to provide a tool which allows individuals and organisations to be more effective by having support for their activities. In this situation, shortcomings in the nature of systems cannot be disguised in modified operating procedures and in the multiple interfaces, as they can be in data processing. A user in office automation is in full contact with the system and any shortcomings will be revealed. Some will be more immediately noticeable than others but the weaknesses will show and consequently systems will then be used only when necessary.

The nature of systems as they impact the user can be discussed under four headings:

- reliability;
- simplicity and naturalness;
- flexibility;
- adaptability.

### Reliability

The levels of reliability which are currently accepted in the data processing world would in most cases be acceptable in the word processing/document preparation environment. But in the personal information management, electronic mail and information base access activities, failures would mean that such things as diaries, essential operating information, and local subject files would not be available and hence most decision-taking and informal office work would come to a halt.

Whilst the prospect of such consequences exist, user confidence in and commitment to an office automation system will remain limited to the work that is not immediately essential. Another quite natural thing to happen is that users will back up the new system with paper-based files and hard copies of catalogues and manuals, and will go through a period of double-checking every action until full confidence in the system is gained. In this situation one failure will probably destroy user confidence for a long time.

An absence of total confidence in systems will probably result in the use of alternative means of backing-up systems. The use of an alternative storage medium, such as microfilm, however many levels of magnetic storage back up are used, will give that extra security which will release users from some inhibitions in using the system. Perceived reliability is probably the most important short-term attribute of any office automation system; it is the first quality by which users judge the system, and it is only when familiarity and confidence have grown that users look to other considerations. Hence, if a system is not reliable and the information and the tools are not available, it is doubtful that the user will venture very far with the system.

Reliability of systems is being increased; as processor costs fall, modularity and built-in redundancy are increasing. Systems are becoming capable of dynamically re-allocating resources so breakdowns of individual modules do not bring operations to a halt.

The developing solid-state storage devices (such as bubble memory, charge-coupled devices and holographic storage) and the non-impact xerographic printers offer much higher reliability than their current highly mechanical counterparts (the magnetic disk and the impact printers), and they can expect wide usage in the future when costs fall.

Communications network reliability is also increasing with the introduction of data networks and computer-controlled exchanges. Here communication uses services designed for data rather than merely making the best job of existing speech networks.

In some computing and communication systems today, stocks of plug-in replacement modules are held at each user's location, enabling a user to carry out emergency maintenance, thereby keeping the system running. As the costs of such spares fall and the reliance on the electronic office increases then this type of user maintenance will become more common.

## Simplicity and Naturalness

In office automation the objective is to provide tools to support informal office activities. Strict job training is not expected to be necessary; all that will be required is a general skill-training in the basics of keyboards, screens, filing, retrieving, indexes, cross-references and the like. The interface between the machine and the operator must be simple and feel natural to use; we do not want the rigid interface traditional in dp systems.

A system that is awkward to use or over-difficult to learn will fall into disuse. Clerical level users, if organised, will voice disquiet through unions, or will produce a standard of work which is low enough to lead to management dissatisfaction. Management, as users, will have the rank and the individual voice to make effective complaints about a system.

Many users of office automation will be casual users who will only have enough contact with a system to be able to operate something that is both easy to learn and easy to use. Without that simplicity, only limited elements of the system will be used and the full potential benefits will not be realised. On the other hand, some full-time users will be involved and over a period of time they will have developed skills and a level of sophistication to which the system needs to respond; otherwise they will become disenchanted with the apparent unwieldiness of the system.

Hence, a simplicity and naturalness of use must be exhibited by the system for both the casual and the full-time user. The changes brought by office automation are met with enough resistance and scepticism without compounding the problem by introducing systems which are difficult to use.

## Flexibility and Adaptability

Office automation systems, as supportive tools, need to be flexible to be able to evolve with users' requirements. As a user's familiarity and awareness grow, the demands on the system will change. Unlike data processing systems, where a user's changed requirements require redefinition and respecification of the system, office automation systems have to be able to respond so that new requirements are met on an *ad hoc* basis.

Not only will users' changing requirements demand that the

system can evolve but it will also have to change its nature by linking to other equipment. For example a change of function would be involved if a word processor was needed to be linked to a photocomposer.

However complete a set of functions appear to be performed at procurement time, users' requirements will change as familiarity and awareness grow and that set of functions will not then appear so complete. New public services will be offered and these will create new possibilities. Such services are Prestel, the Post Office's viewdata service, and the anticipated public text communication service. Equipment available ought to be capable of being interfaced with these services.

Today's computer-based office products can be flexible and adaptable. They can exhibit simple and natural interfaces, with high reliability. However, these products are being sold to meet today's requirements, and are being sold in a competitive market, so seemingly unnecessary enhancements and capabilities are not being built into machines. In addition whilst there is no effective demand for the extra capabilities they will not be included unless the cost of doing so is marginal or it is a good commercial ploy.

In conclusion, reliability, simplicity, flexibility and adaptability will be important factors in the success of office automation systems. Without them, office automation will have little use beyond word processing and document preparation. But at the moment costs are such that not too much emphasis can be put on these factors by manufacturers. Fortunately costs are falling and performance capability is rising.

## AUTHORISATION AND AUTHENTICATION

The level of use of electronic message or information systems will in part reflect the degree of confidence that users have in the authenticity of the message and the authorisation given to that message. Most of the doubts expressed are based on a quite natural hesitancy on changing from today's familiar and very real paper system to the abstract world of magnetic storage and electronic transmission.

Paper-based messages can be readily identified as originals; they also contain unique signatures or official stamps. The authenticity is further reinforced by headed notepaper and envelopes and by postmarks and franking marks.

In electronic transmissions, the information appears on your own screen and if printed appears on your own paper. There may be a name on the bottom of the message but there is no signature. The original form of the message cannot be examined for changes made after authorisation, as can a paper-based message.

But how many of these things are real problems, how much does a signature really mean to the recipient of a message? A signature is unique and can be compared, but how often does a comparator exist for the signature? How often is a signature examined and how often are letters received and signed per procurationem? The authorisation and authentication of the majority of messages is verified by circumstantial evidence, such as the letter being expected and the contents being reasonable. If the message is not expected and the contents do not seem reasonable then further enquiries are made to verify authenticity and authorisation.

However, there are messages such as financial transactions where authorisation is necessary. The Telex system is widely used for financial transactions and here authorisation codes as agreed between sender and recipient are used. There is no reason why these sorts of arrangements should not be used in future systems for those messages where authorisation is necessary.

If future text communication services, being proposed by telephone authorities throughout the world, come into being then it is likely that all messages transmitted will have sending terminal code and date added by the service and this will probably be sufficient an authentication aid for the majority of messages and users of the system. Nevertheless many documents today do bear signatures. Many rules and laws exist which insist on original papers carrying signatures being available and people are accustomed to seeing signatures. Because of these factors the tradition of using signatures can be expected to continue for a long time, and indeed with computer assistance, signature-verification systems may be able to make more valid comparisons of signatures than can the human eye.

IBM has developed a system which will measure a signature in terms of pen pressure and acceleration at the time of writing and compares the data with reference data collected from a sample signature.[1] This type of system would permit a message service to hold a bank of reference signatures to be compared with the

[1] Computer Weekly 5 Oct 78

signature of the sender of the message and then although that signature did not appear to the recipient the message service could advise the recipient that an acceptable signature was made at the time of despatch.

## REGULATORY LIMITATIONS

In most of the world except the USA the carriage of data by tele-communications is a statutory monopoly of the PTTs (postal, telegraph and telephone authorities). In the USA, data is carried by the common carriers who are licenced for that purpose by the Federal Communications Commission. These common carriers in turn will allow other concerns to use those carriage facilities to provide enhanced data communications service for the public. These are called Value-Added Services. In the UK the monopoly position of carriage held by the British Post Office is further reinforced by rules which forbid the provision of message facilities by one body on behalf of others, ie third party message switching. Additionally the Post Office has the right to insist that all equipment being attached to its network is electrically and operationally suitable for connection to those networks, and in the interests of all users the rules governing approval are rigidly applied.

The monopolistic position of the Post Office as the sole data carrier, the third party switching rules, the attachment regulations and the level of services actually provided by the PO have been the subject of public discussion. The report of the National Committee on Computer Networks in 1978[1] included the following recommendations:

- That the need for a Public Switched Data Transmission Service (PSDS) in the UK, with international connections and to international standards is important and urgent, and that this service should be provided and operated by the PO, and that a service based on packet-switching techniques should be the first step.

- A more liberal attitude should be taken towards attachments, and the Post Office monopoly on the provision of modems for connection to the Public Switched Telephone Network should be removed.

- A limited offer of licences should be made to allow the setting-up of message switching services over Post Office lines as a private commercial venture.

[1] DOI/NCCN 1978

The current restriction on third-party switching, together with the fact that the PO provides no more than a basic data transmission service, excludes UK users from considering the timesharing approach in fulfilling the third-party switching aspects of office automation. In the USA, systems such as AUGMENT, provided by Tymshare Inc, offer document preparation, electronic mail, personal filing and data base access facilities through the TYMNET network. By virtue of network interconnection, access to users and information on other networks worldwide is also possible. Similar systems provide computer conferencing facilities, eg PLANET/FORUM by Tymshare, and these too are not available in the UK and Western Europe.

Compatibility services are provided on value-added networks in the USA; these services allow different terminal types to interconnect. The current position on standardisation is providing a large market for these facilities, with networks offering word processor compatibility and facsimile compatibility across the USA. Currently such services for public use cannot be provided in the UK by any body other than the Post Office.

The attachment policy of the Post Office has in the past insisted on the use of Post Office supplied modems on the PSTN, except where the facilities of a privately supplied modem are significantly different from a PO supplied modem. It did not permit modems to be built into data terminals, for use on any PSTN transmission lines, though it is permitted to use equipment with integral modems on leased transmission lines, provided of course that the equipment has been approved as electrically and operationally suitable. The PO's attachment policy has been relaxed in allowing the integration of modems into the television sets being built for use with the Prestel viewdata system. Now that the precedent has been set this will lead to pressure from data terminal manufacturers for similar relaxations to be made for their equipment. This policy is also reflected in the separation of voice telephone handsets (maintained by PO engineers) and data terminals (maintained by manufacturer). This ruling excludes the equipment typified by the Nixdorf 8811 DATATEL, a microprocessor-based piece of equipment which offers data collection, file enquiry with voice response and ordinary voice facilities through a common handset. The attachment ruling is though considered essential where it concerns engineering approval.

These restrictions on the services that can be provided by other bodies, together with the current lack of provision of advanced services by the PO could present quite a hurdle to those wishing to move into inter-company office automation in the near future. However the PO has announced plans for the introduction of a Public Packet Switched Service (PSS) in 1980 and for a phased implementation of an integrated digital network (System X), capable of transmitting text, data, speech, video and facsimile with equal facility. This is scheduled for introduction in the mid-1980s.

In the case of value-added services, it is doubtful that the PO would wish to relax the third-party switching restriction, but there are indications that a number of PTTs acting through the CCITT (International Telegraph and Telephone Consultative Committee) are interested in providing value-added services themselves. The Teletex text communication service being defined in CCITT will probably be the first of these. It is important to emphasise that the two success stories of telecommunications — telephone and telex — which Teletex is likely to follow, have both been the product of international debate and agreement between PTTs and that standards and their enforcement are the essential elements of such an agreement. It is difficult to envisage any future network being capable of offering the extensive coverage necessary for success without that international agreement and without the rigid enforcement of standards by the PTTs.

## OPERATIONAL SUPPORT

The operational support requirements of an office automation system are similar to those of traditional data processing, except that a wider variety of people is being expected to perform the support procedures. Currently this area of operational support is much underplayed and yet is terribly important to the continued success of an office system.

Files of documents have to be organised and logged; retention, deletion and archiving policies have to be developed and implemented; security of information has to be attended to and the privacy requirements of individuals and work areas must be recognised with passwords allocated and controlled. These types of procedures, commonplace in data processing, are implemented and performed by a limited number of highly trained people. By contrast, in office automation, people without technical skills and knowledge, and people whose interest is in office practice, will have to ensure that such procedures are followed.

The knowledge and skills required by the operators will depend upon the nature of the systems. Systems which are situated within each work area, and where work-stations are widely dispersed will require each user to be familiar and competent with the procedures. Whereas in the equipment pool environment, more operation-support responsibility can be given to the supervisors than to the operators, in the timesharing environment, either in-house or through a 'public service', then the majority of the responsibility rests with the providers of the service.

Operational support does cost money to implement and operate, but without it information files will be lost or corrupted, information will be illegally accessed or not archived, and in consequence user confidence and level of use of the system will fall.

## UNCONTROLLED PROCUREMENT

The cost of equipment and services is dropping to such an extent that purchases are being made from departmental budgets without reference to corporate policies or strategies. For example, the PET personal computer retails at £400, the Olivetti ET201 intelligent typewriter is sold at £1,075, whilst the Memotext word processor sells at about £3,000. The fact that costs are still dropping was illustrated in early-1979 when Xerox reduced the purchase price of its word processors by 20%.

In this situation a wide variety of incompatible equipment will be introduced to an organisation without reference to any overall objectives. Each piece of kit will be used to meet task requirements alone and will probably not be capable of addressing the needs of the organisation as a whole. Storage media will be different and not capable of being transferred from machine to machine. There is likely to be a variation in character codes and command codes so that even if some machines have communication facilities it will be a matter of luck if they can communicate in a meaningful manner. Any application systems developed will not be able to be transferred and would have to be rewritten for use elsewhere.

This proliferation of equipment will occur through the good intentions of each department and can probably only be avoided through the establishment of a corporate strategy. The problem areas mentioned will be of little consequence whilst people are only concerned with automated typing, but once reference files of customers, eg names and addresses, are created and users are wanting to transfer information then problems start to occur and information has to be printed out from one system and rekeyed into another. Whilst some benefits of office automation which require no communication and no transfer of data or text may be

obtained, uncontrolled procurement will inhibit users from
realising the full benefit and making the most of office automation
opportunities.

# 5  Implementation

The process of implementing the electronic office can draw upon the experiences of data processing in that both are concerned with the introduction of technology. However, whilst the lessons learnt by dp should not be ignored there are factors which demand a different approach to implementation.

Firstly the wider benefits of the electronic office are not easy to quantify and therefore investment managers may not be sympathetic. In such circumstances, top management are going to be asked to take a new look at the organisation and its objectives.

Secondly the electronic office has potential at all levels of every staff function in an organisation. In order to ensure that a complete job is done, not only must all functions be considered but all functions must be represented in the construction of an implementation plan.

Finally the electronic office is a set of flexible tools rather than a strict mechanistic procedure. It will have a direct impact on people, their cultures and the organisational structures.

This chapter suggests ways in which implementation of the electronic office should proceed from the establishment of a corporate strategy to the review of jobs.

Although what is looked at here is the implementation of systems aimed at achieving the full benefits of the electronic office, many organisations will be installing pure word processing and other single elements of automation systems. Whilst in this situation the top-down objective identity exercise suggested here will not be justified, many of the points made are as important in the small typing pool implementation as they are in the company-wide integrated management support systems.

129

## MAXIMISATION OF OPPORTUNITIES

To realise the benefits of office automation, top management have to think in terms of maximising opportunities rather than minimising costs. Traditionally investment is guided by cost minimisation and this is particularly so in the office environment. The creed has been — *reduce costs by introducing the minimum technology*. This approach was adopted in the era of cheap people and expensive equipment. Now the picture is changing dramatically; we must consider making the best use of people's time and giving them the support they need to work effectively. Giving the support required means that employees can give more of their time to using the information and less time in collecting, updating, storing, retrieving and communicating.

The cost-saving approach which is driving most of the current implementations of word processors achieves few of the wider benefits of office automation. Even though the level of savings actually made by staff cuts or by increased throughput is in many instances not insignificant, eg Bank of America saves £3 million p.a., they are minimal when compared to the possibilities of full office automation. However, whilst office investment attitudes are such that definite cost saving must be demonstrated, then the real opportunities of office automation will either be ignored or will be hidden beneath the savings of staff displacement.

The opportunities of office automation are mostly concerned with information, its value to the organisation, and the part that the information plays in the production of goods or services. Top management must accept that, as in the factory and as on the farm, investment in the office is required to create those opportunities. It has been estimated[1] that annual investment in capital equipment per office worker in the US is $2000 compared with $25,000 per year for each manufacturing employee.

Attitudes which have evolved through years of business experience cannot be expected to accommodate immediately the changes being created by the advances in microprocessors and communications. Therefore approaches to office automation will have to recognise this. Senior management needs to be made aware of the changes that are occurring and of the opportunities that these create. Without such awareness, no investment plan

[1] Purchase 1978

relying on anything but the most tangible cost benefits will be accepted. Even after awareness has been created, the investment manager will be sceptical about any plan without a substantial proportion of quantifiable benefits.

This attitude of looking at cost minimisation rather than at opportunity maximisation is one that will be prevalent until opportunity maximisation has been clearly demonstrated to be the right approach. As ever it will be the few innovative organisations who, committing the resources and reaping the commercial benefits, demonstrate the success.

## RESTATEMENT OF BUSINESS OBJECTIVES

A restatement by senior management of the business objectives of the organisation and the methods of achieving those objectives is an essential framework within which to formulate any office automation plans.

Without such a statement there will be a tendency to look at task requirements alone, without reference to the corporate objectives. There is always a temptation to apply new technology to old problems and end up doing business as usual with new kit. In most cases this will not address the true requirements of the organisation and will leave many areas of opportunity untouched. The tasks currently performed in an organisation have developed over a period of time and have been moulded by both political and technological forces. Consequently in relation to the business objectives some tasks will have assumed a disproportionate importance and some will no longer be relevant. Therefore some redefinition of tasks may be necessary within the formulation of plans.

Plans that are formulated within senior management's own statement of business objectives will provide more justification than plans which refer purely to the planning team's observations and informed opinions. The opportunities offered by office automation, even though the benefits are largely unquantifiable, will assume some greater importance when related to the achievement of business objectives.

The corporate strategy that is developed must relate to all functions of the organisation with no one function being treated separately and all with reference to the business objectives. The corporate strategy has to have the commitment of senior management, in terms of time, people and money, and then be presented to line management. The alternative to an accepted corporate strategy will be the uncontrolled procurement of a whole variety of incompatible equipment, addressing a host of individual task requirements and probably reducing the effectiveness of the organisation as a whole.

## IDENTIFY CONTRIBUTION OF PEOPLE

The restatement of business objectives and fundamental activities is the first step in implementing the electronic office by looking at the organisation from the top downwards. It provides a reference frame within which all plans and work items can be placed. The next level of detail concerns identifying the contribution of people and the support they need. Here the work items within the fundamental activities, the people involved and their skills, the structures and cultures of the work areas, and the attitudes of individuals and collective groups, need to be studied and appreciated.

Such investigations will facilitate the formulation of work area plans which will have considered the following:

— the degree of support needed and the benefits to stem from that support;

— the level of awareness of the possibilities;

— the skills used in the current work areas;

— the degree of resistance/acceptance likely to be exhibited by people in work areas.

The amount of support needed, and the benefits to the organisation stemming from that support, will indicate some degree of priority for phasing implementation. The professional consultant engineer, heavily involved in discussion, collaboration, retrieval and storage of technical information, may require a lot of support. That support may increase his personal contribution fivefold, whereas the managing director, requiring much less support, wanting access to far fewer facilities, may realise the same degree of corporate benefits as the engineer. The nature of the support required will also vary according to discipline; for example, the public relations employee, in the world of tight deadlines and ever-changing copy, may want more immediate support than will the business strategist. Business structures and cultures will also influence the nature of the support required. A work area that is formal, deadly efficient and has been autocratically run for years, will respond in a totally different way than the individuals in an informal less-mechanistic environment.

The degree of awareness of the electronic office and its possibilities shown by different groups of people will to a large extent indicate the size of the education programme which will have to be mounted. A high level of awareness will most likely be reflected in the easy acceptance of the new ways of working. When coupled with enthusiasm, this awareness will indicate people who are likely to explore the system facilities and use the system to the full.

The skills currently used by people in a work area and the values currently placed on those skills compared with the skills required in a new environment will indicate the amount of retraining required. A reduction in the value of hard learnt and respected skills is no small thing to present to a person, and the offer of retraining to replace that skill with another of equal status and equal value will be necessary.

The degree of resistance/acceptance likely to be exhibited by people in work areas will be a reflection of several factors. If the work area is one concerned with technology or with instituting change itself then there is likely to be a high degree of acceptance; well-established professions with recognised ways of working will be less receptive.

Age has been shown to be of great importance in accepting change. Whilst there can be no clean demarcation it is generally reckoned that people above the age of 40 should not be expected to accept change easily. A different response therefore should be expected from a high technology research unit with an average age of 30 than from a group of senior bankers aged 60 and over.

Varying cultures in an organisation will also be reflected in the acceptance of change; for example, a sales team who are constantly competing with each other for the best sales figures are going to be keen to remain as competitive as their fellows and use any support offered, whereas line managers who are not directly on performance rewards will probably be more hesitant to accept change.

Any feeling of insecurity in the people to be affected will also generate a good deal of resistance. The feelings may be caused by thoughts of staff cuts or job-content changes, work pattern changes or changes in skill value. The feelings of insecurity may stem from a lack of awareness or from genuine worries. Whatever the case, those feelings cannot be ignored and show the need for an education, training and staffing policy to be included in the office automation plan. This policy should be developed and agreed with staff and their representatives.

Having studied the work areas and the people, and having gained an understanding of the support needed, the possible benefits, the level of awareness, the skills and the likely degree of resistance it is then possible to start considering a plan for introducing the electronic office.

It is important to remember that the changes being suggested are ones that could make some very basic alterations in the way people work, the way they interact, and the responsibilities they hold. Consequently, from the very early days in the formulation of strategies, an effort should be made to involve staff, management and their representatives as a real part of the process. It is likely that in most work areas the awareness of the electronic office will be low and early user involvement will not only provide an innocent sounding-board for ideas and a source of opinion, but will also help in the growth of awareness in the work areas, even before any education programme has been formulated.

It is at this stage that manufacturers and vendors of equipment become involved, and development teams will be pressed into attending exhibitions and demonstrations set up by the vendors. If possible it is better to avoid that sterile demonstration environment and see the equipment installed and operational in another user company. Talks with those users at all levels; manager to manager; supervisor to supervisor; operator to operator will always be beneficial. Some fears can be allayed, others will be reinforced, and again awareness will increase. The experience of others, although not always directly relevant, usually has something to offer.

## CROSS-FUNCTION REPRESENTATION

The team responsible for developing office automation plans needs to represent the interests of all of staff functions, ie data processing, office administration and communications. They may be separate at the moment or they may be combined under 'management services' or 'information services'. The concept of office automation embraces all of those functions and it is doubtful whether any of them could do a complete job alone.

Data processing traditionally provides systems with many layers of interface between user and system, whereas in office automation we are talking about a direct interaction between user and tool. As a result of data processing traditions, many dp ventures into office systems have been disasters, failing because they presented unnatural interfaces to users and required rigid proceddures to be followed and strict job training to be undertaken.

Office administrators do know what makes offices tick, but generally they lack the technical awareness and experience possessed by data processing staff. This experience and awareness of technical possibilities is essential when laying the foundations of any office automation plan.

Office communications, which usually embraces the post room, the mail service, telex and telephone switchboard, has always been able to provide a good service whilst acting as an independent function; increasingly, communications services are linking directly with other functions, and independent action may leave areas of opportunity unaddressed or result in duplication of effort. Word processors can now link to telex machines, the telephone exchange can provide data communication facilities, company data bases can provide information on word processors; and all functions need to be involved in the development of a corporate strategy for office automation.

## EXPERIMENTATION AND PHASED EXPANSION

The technological problems in the introduction of the electronic office are minor by comparison with the organisational, structural and personnel problems likely to occur. Because of this the organisation and the people need to be prepared for the changes which cause the problems. Experimentation and phased expansion will reduce the trauma of the changes and will help avoid the possibility of a mismatch of the system against the organisation.

Experimentation gives an opportunity to iron out problems that would be fatal in a full system. The reactions of people and the organisation to various work patterns and structures can be monitored. The people involved can have the opportunity to voice their opinions, knowing that they will be valued and that this may have some affect on the shape of the experiment in the future.

Awareness will be increased by experimentation in a work environment far more than it will be by education programmes and demonstrations. The experiments should occur in an operational environment, using people with skills representative of the work area as a whole, rather than using technical people with special skills. They should suffer the normal working pressures such as deadlines and peak workloads: an experiment in a cocoon will yield very few useful results, other than those results concerned with the technology of the situation. If possible, choose the people to be part of the experiments. Careful selection is not suggested for the purpose of spreading propaganda about a bad system, but for the purpose of sharing the experience of using the system.

Those chosen should be key people in the social infrastructure of the organisation; the people who will chat about their use of the system, who will invite others to 'have a go', who will be able to arrive at reasoned opinions of their whole involvement. Wherever possible, these key people should be carefully chosen at all levels, including management, supervisors and operators. Avoid the person who is an isolationist; true he may be very effective and his contribution to the organisation could be increased by the use of office automation, but for the purposes of the experiment his sharing of experiences with his peers and the collection of opinions are likely to be limited.

Any union involvement will have started at a much earlier stage than the experimentation and it is unlikely that any problems will be caused by nomination of official representatives as experimenters. A much more likely problem will be the political manoeuvring of functional management in trying to get their departments involved in experiments.

Careful accounting of experiments should be performed, as the results may be able to help quantify some of the benefits which were previously thought intangible. If possible, the construction of an acceptable productivity measure, before any experiments are started, would provide even more quantitative evidence. However, clerical productivity measurement schemes applied to individuals are not usually viewed favourably by unions and any measurements may have to be restricted to the level of whole work areas.

Currently electronic office equipment is not available as a complete system from a single supplier. All the technology exists but some of it needs further refinement. Costs are still fairly high but they are falling. Communications facilities are becoming even more capable of providing the speed and the flexibility that will be required in the electronic office. In the above sort of environment, experimentation does more than create awareness and take the sharp edge from the introduction of change; it permits organisations to prepare themselves to be ready to take advantage of the situation when the total electronic office is available as an off-the-shelf product at the right price with the right communications services to support it.

Research and development investment in the office is not the accepted practice today and experimentation is expensive but the acquisition of experience now by experimentation will enable the full opportunities of tomorrow to be taken. Any experiment which is successful in technical, organisation and structural terms, should not be assumed to apply to the whole organisation. Structures, cultures and attitudes in different work areas will vary and these will shape the reactions of people towards a system and will shape the requirements they have to any system.

Systems need to be expanded with care and expanded in small discrete steps. Quantum step changes are unnecessary in office systems and will only serve to antagonise the users and hence condemn the system to failure. The experimentation and the expansion of electronic office systems should be monitored and modified continually, the users must not feel constrained by a system; what is being offered is a tool to augment the ability that already exists, and feelings of constraint will reduce the individuals use of the system.

The use of experimentation to introduce change indicates a recognition of the tremendous inertia that exists in the traditional working methods, structures and attitudes which have built up over the years. Moreover that it takes an appropriate length of time for the acceptance of changes to those traditions and that resistance will be generated by forcing people unwillingly into a face-to-face situation with those changes.

## TRAINING AND EDUCATION

Unlike in data processing systems, where users require a specific job training, what is required for the electronic office is a general awareness of the concepts and the equipment and general skill training in the use of the equipment. This is in addition to the specific knowledge of the work area. The electronic office will be impacting directly a far greater number of people and a far wider range of people than did traditional data processing. Consequently the basic education system should be reviewed to include a general awareness programme for the concepts and equipment of the electronic office and also general skill training for keyboards and other basic equipment. Until such a review does occur, the total education and training programme will have to be organised by users.

Currently vendors of equipment provide limited 'get to know our system' type of training sessions, but the basic awareness education is a prerequisite to that, and has to begin as soon as a corporate strategy is considered. This education programme should be continued through the experimentation phase, when experience being shared in a working environment can supplement the more formal programmes.

General skill training may cause some problems in the short term; somebody may have to acquire a skill which they have not considered necessary. For example, some managers will feel that typing is demeaning. After all secretaries do all the typing and filing, and managers do none. Similarly, many typists may not wish to lose their hard-learnt clean-copy typing ability. Forcing people to change skills will not ease the situation. Alternatives have to be offered; the manager may be perfectly happy if the secretary is a 'technical interface', and the typist may be happy to use traditional skills in another department. But skill training is required for systems to be successful. The low use of many centralised dictation systems has been attributed to potential users feeling untrained and not wishing to make fools of themselves.

The electronic office will introduce new concepts and items of equipment. Education programmes and the sharing of experience will build up familiarity, awareness and confidence, but without the necessary skill training, many systems will remain underutilised and unexploited.

## JOB REVIEWS

Changes wrought by office automation on organisational structures, job content, work patterns and skill values need to be appreciated by both the implementation team and the user. This appreciation is needed so that a personnel programme acceptable to management, user and unions can be developed. Such a personnel programme is needed to enable:

- people to be matched with jobs;
- career-development plans to be established;
- training requirements to be identified;
- development of equitable salary and wage plans.

The development of a personnel programme for office systems which is consistent with the systems design and the organisation's overall personnel policy is an important part of an office automation implementation plan. In the development of the personnel programme the following activities should be included:

- job analysis;

- job description;
- job evaluation;
- career development.

Job analysis is the process of identifying all the tasks encompassing a job, however trivial or complex, and examining each task in detail. All tasks should be analysed in relation to skill, knowledge and experience requirements; to the complexity of the task; to the importance of the task to the organisation; to the responsibilities assumed in performing the task; to the contacts and relationships made inside and outside; and to the initiative required to be displayed in performance of the task. The job analysis would normally be performed by a job analyst in close cooperation with the current job holder, and the results will enable a job description to be prepared.

Job descriptions should be complete, exact, simple, clear and distinguishable from others. This will enable jobs and people to be matched, thereby ensuring the needed level of performance and providing a greater degree of job satisfaction. A secretary's role perception may be much lower than the principal's expectation when the job description is not accurate and complete. Job descriptions may be written by the holders of the job, the supervisor or the design team, or by a job analyst, but should always be finalised with a trained job analyst. The job description provides the basis for the job-evaluation procedure.

Job evaluation is not a method of valuing a person — it is the valuing of the job. A common system used for evaluating jobs is a points system where factors common to a range of jobs are identified and points are awarded according to how strongly those factors appear in the jobs. For example, the factors chosen by Barclays Bank International together with NUBE (National Union of Bank Employees) in their secretarial job evaluation scheme were skills, supervision, confidential information, contact and initiative. The complete job evaluation provides the basis for the establishment of an equitable salary plan for a range of jobs and the establishment of a career-development programme.

The career-development programme should identify the differences between levels so that movements can be seen as true career advancements. Such a programme can influence employee motivation by firstly, providing an employee with performance understanding; secondly, establishing the range of opportunities; and thirdly, identifying the attributes required to achieve movement on career paths. It should always be clear that movement on the career paths will not necessarily follow a rigid time scale.

The points discussed above have not related at all to the holders of the jobs; even so, during a time of change, the relative positions of jobs may shift and some current job holders would probably be unhappy. There are several solutions to this problem; firstly, retraining of the holder so that a job on the new scale of equivalent reward, satisfaction and prospects to the old job can be entered; secondly, paying current job holders at the level of the old scales; and thirdly, having an appeals procedure so that the job evaluations can be challenged and re-examined. Any appeals procedure should be established when the personnel programme is first developed.

In all the four areas of job analysis, job description, job evaluation and career development, as in the remainder of the electronic office implementation plan, user involvement is imperative if the personnel programme is to facilitate change.

# 6 The Future

Technology is advancing in quantum steps. This can be witnessed with the microprocessor and communications, but the application of that technology in the office will not follow in anything like the same manner. Movements towards the electronic office will in general be evolutionary rather than revolutionary.

The steadying influences on the introduction of technology were discussed in Chapter 4. These include what is common in all change situations, the powerful inertia in the existing practices. Because of this inertia, the old way of working has to be unqualifiably demonstrated to be ineffective and uneconomic before any new way of working will be adopted. Similarly, there is an inertia which naturally resists changes required of existing attitudes. There is though a constant movement towards the electronic office. Elements of it are in use today, and more and more of the facilities are being integrated into single products.

Considering the various factors inhibiting and driving development of office automation, five possible milestones in the evolution towards the electronic office are outlined:

- Document preparation using word processors and photo-typesetters exists in an expanding market. It is likely to be, for most organisations, the first step in office automation.

- The second step is likely to be establishing access to data and information bases. This would be done initially by linking to in-house data base facilities. Using facilities outside the organisation would come later.

- The next evolutionary step will probably be intra-company mail.

- This would be followed by access to external data and information bases.

– To be followed finally by an inter-company mail facility.

The sequence of those milestones will reflect the effort involved on the part of the organisation, and also the effort involved on the part of the user in accepting the changes.

The first two are entirely within the control of the company. No collaboration with external organisations is required, and problems of standards can for the most part be avoided by the use of a single equipment supplier. The use of data and information bases considerably enhances the potential of the word processor, permitting personal information filing and access to and storage of a wider range of information.

The third step, the intra-company mail, involves the organisation in spreading terminals around the organisation and involves the user in a change in working habits.

The fourth step, external data and information base access, involves the organisation with other bodies; shortage of standards may cause compatibility problems. Although dependent upon the speed of evolution all manufacturers may by that time conform to Public Data Network Standards or Public Data Networks may offer compatibility services which allow the use of any manufacturer's terminal.

The final stage, inter-company mail, can only be expected to perform at a satisfactory level on a global scale, if a public service is provided and standards are imposed. Otherwise, so many variations in traditions and practices exist (eg paper sizes, character sets, etc) as to make the system unworkable.

The above scenario considered progress towards the electronic office for the organisation as a whole. But that progress will not be uniform; it will initially be used to support clerical activity, where benefits are easier to cost. Only after it has been observed in the clerical area, and awareness has grown, will it be used to support management activities. Then it may have to be used by the secretaries first before the managers feel that they could benefit from personal use. After all, it's not done for managers to type, is it?

# Bibliography

Anderson, Howard, What is Electronic Mail?, *Telecommunications*, November 1978

APEX (Association of Professional, Executive, Clerical and Computer Staff), *Office Technology — The Trade Union Response*, March 1979

Bedwekk, C. H., *Viewing Visual Display Units*, presented at Ergonomics Society Seminar, 15/12/78

Bleazard, G. B., *Why Packet Switching?* NCC Publications, 1979

Business Monitor PQ481, Paper and Board, 3rd Quarter 1978

Cakir, I. A., *The Incidence and Importance of Eye Strain Among VDU Operators*, presented at Ergonomics Society Seminar, 15/12/78

CEPT/Eurodata Foundation, *Public Data Networks — Plans of the European Telecommunications Administrations*, 1978

Collinge, B., *BLAISE — The British Library Automated Information Service*, Aslib Proceedings, 30 (10-11), October-November 1978, pp 394-402

*Department of Employment Gazette*, July 1978

*Department of Employment Gazette*, August 1978

*Department of Employment Gazette*, December 1978

DOI/NCCN, *Report of the National Committee on Computer Networks*, 1978

Field, Robert B., Advanced Message System, *Telecommunications*, October 1977

Hall, J. L., *On-Line Information Retrieval Source Book*, ASLIB, 1978

143

Hugo, I. St. J., *Guide to Word Processing Systems 1979,* Computer Guides Ltd., 1979

Jenkins, Clive & Sherman, Barrie, *The Collapse of Work,* Eyre Methuen, 1979

Kemp, G. S., VANS in Europe, *Telecommunications,* July 1978

Lurin, E. S. & Metz, E., Get Ready for VANS, *Datamation,* July 1978

Moss, C. E. et al, *A Report on Electromagnetic Radiation Surveys of Video Display Terminals,* National Institute of Occupational Safety and Health, December 1977

NCC Information Services
 - *Computing Journal Abstracts,* specific subject search or fortnightly bulletin
 - *Computer Hardware Record,* specific equipment search or sets of abstracts; relevant titles include:
   - *Electronic Office Equipment* (Word Processors, Facsimile Equipment, Programmable Calculators), February 1979
   - *Character Recognition Equipment,* April 1979
   - *COM Equipment, Microfilm Microfiche Readers,* March 1978

Nilles, J. M., *The Telecommunication-Transportation Trade-Off,* Wiley, 1976

Parker, E. B. & Porat, M., *Social Implications of Computer/ Telecommunication Systems,* Report 16, Stanford University, 1975

Pugh, A. R., British Post Office, *International Facsimile Transmission and Standards,* IGC Conference, Amsterdam, September 1978

Purchase, A., *Office of the Future,* SRI Business Intelligence Program Guidelines, April 1978

Pye, R., Communications Studies and Planning Ltd., *Telecommunications and the Electronic Office,* ISL Conference, January 1979

Robinson, A. H., & Bence, A. T., Forward Step for Facsimile, *PO Telecomms Journal,* Summer 1978

Scott, P. R. D., *Introducing Data Communications Standards,* NCC Publications, 1979

Simons, G. L., *Introducing Microprocessors*, NCC Publications, 1979

SITPRO, *Future Trends in Computer and Communications Systems*, SITPRO, 1978

Stamps, G. M., *Facsimile as a Business*, IGC Conference, Facsimile in Tomorrow's Organisation, Amsterdam, September 1978

Stewart, T. F. M. (1), *Humanising Word Processing*, presented at On-Line Conference,June 1978

Stewart, T. F. M. (2), *VDU Ergonomics and Eye Strain*, presented at Ergonomics Society Seminar, 15/12/78

Turoff, Murray N., *Computerised Conferencing and Real-Time Delphis: Unique Communications Forms*, Proceedings of the Second International Conference on Computer Communications, August 1974 (ICCC PO Box 9745, Washington DC 20016)

Turoff, Murray, & Hiltz, Starr Roxanne, Meeting Through Your Computer, *Spectrum*, May 1977

Uhlig, R. P., Human Factors in Computer Message Systems, *Datamation*, May 1977

White, R. B., A Prototype for the Electronic Office, *Datamation*, April 1977

White, C. E., A.T. & T.'s ACS, *Telecommunications*, February 1979

Wilkins, A. J., *Epileptogenic Attributes of TV and VDUs*, presented at Ergonomic Society Seminar, 15/12/78

Williamson, J., The Booming Telex Business, *Telecommunications*, February 1978

Wood, M. B., *Word Processing at The National Computing Centre – Two Years' Experience*, Status Report, NCC Publications, 1979

# Glossary of Acronyms

| | |
|---|---|
| ANSI | — American National Standards Institute. |
| APEX | — Association of Professional, Executive, Clerical and Computer Staff. |
| ARPANET | — A packet switched network commissioned by the Advanced Research Projects Agency of the US Department of Defence. |
| ASLIB | — Association of Special Libraries and Information Bureau. |
| ASTMS | — Association of Scientific, Technical and Managerial Staff. |
| BLAISE | — British Library Automated Information Service. |
| BSI | — British Standards Institution. |
| CCITT | — International Telegraph and Telephone Consultative Committee. |
| CEPT | — European Conference on Posts and Telecommunications. |
| COM | — Computer Output to Microfilm. |
| CPU | — Central Processing Unit. Carries out the logic and arithmetic functions of computers and supplies control signals. |
| CRT | — Cathode Ray Tube. One provision of the screen in visual display units. |
| DC | — Draft for Comment (BSI). An early stage of a British Standard. |
| DD | — Draft for Development (BSI). A pilot for an eventual British Standard. Often produced to meet an urgent need. |

| DIS | – Draft International Standard (ISO). The final stage of an international standard before agreement. |
| DN-1 | – The proposed Netherlands packet switched network. |
| DP | – Draft Proposal (ISO). An early stage of an international standard. |
| EBCDIC | – Extended Binary Coded Decimal Interchange Code (an IBM 'standard'). |
| ECMA | – European Computer Manufacturers Association. |
| ESA-SDS | – European Space Agency – Space Documentation Service. An information supply service. |
| EURONET | – A European packet switched network commissioned by the EEC to meet the need and growth of traffic accessing information bases. |
| IEC | – International Electrotechnical Committee. Safety and standardisation aspects of electrical equipment. |
| IEEE | – Institute of Electrical and Electronics Engineers (USA). |
| IPSS | – International Packet Switched Service of the British P.O. The UK gateway to other packet switched networks. |
| ISO | – International Organisation for Standardisation. |
| NASA | – National Aeronautics and Space Administration (USA). |
| NCCN | – National Committee on Computer Networks. |
| NPDN | – The proposed Nordic packet switched network, serving Denmark, Finland, Norway and Sweden. |
| OCR | – Optical Character Recognition. |
| OCR-A | – Optical Character Recognition Set A. A highly stylised font of the numerals and four special symbols. |

| | |
|---|---|
| OCR-B | – Optical Character Recognition Set B. A complete alphanumeric font with both capital and small letters. |
| PBX | – Private Branch Exchange. The private telephone exchange linking an in-house telephone system with the public switched telephone network. Increasingly these are computer controlled, depending heavily on microprocessors. |
| PD | – Published Document (BSI). Produced when a standard is not agreed, but the information is considered to be of use. |
| PSS | – Packet Switched Service of the British Post Office. |
| PSTN | – Public Switched Telephone Network. |
| PTT | – Post, Telegraph and Telephone Authority. |
| RETD | – The Spanish packet switched network. |
| SDC | – Systems Development Corporation. A US-based information supply service. |
| SI | – The International System of Units. |
| SITPRO | – Simplification of International Trade Procedures Board. Was set up in June 1970 to "guide, stimulate and assist the rationalisation of international trade procedures and the documentation and information flows associated with them .... particularly in view of the widening use of computers and communications links". |
| SYSTEM X | – The British Post Office's program for digitisation of the telecommunications network. |
| TRANSPAC | – The French national packet switch network. |
| VANS | – Value Added Network Service. A communications network service which does more than merely transmit information. |
| VDU | – Visual Display Unit. Consists of a display screen, the controlling electronics, screen housing and often incorporates a keyboard. The screen could be a cathode ray tube |

(CRT), a gas plasma display, a light emitting diode (LED), or a liquid crystal display (LCD).

X25                    – A CCITT recommendation which defines the connection of terminals to packet switch network.

# Index

151

costs;
    office rents
    office supplies,
    transportation                        9
costs, staff                      3-5, 16
cost-saving applications       14-15, 110-112, 130-131
credit checking               60, 61
cross-function representation    134-135
cross-referencing            72, 80, 85
current activity              17-19
customised compatibility       92

daisy-wheel printer          40
data base                  7, 11, 12, 14, 25, 61, 62, 141, 142
data collection              26, 61, 63, 73, 75, 78, 125
data communication regulations  27, 33, 54, 59, 61, 81, 87
data communications standards  90, 100-101
data enquiry              25, 73, 75
Data General             56
data processing             11, 25, 26, 62, 75, 94, 119, 121, 126, 129, 134
data representation standards  91, 95
data terminal             60, 73, 75, 125
de facto standards         93
Dest Data Corporation     77
Diablo                 40
Digital Equipment Corporation  81, 85
digitised images          21, 26, 52, 81
disk                  39, 41
disk cartridge            97
diskette (flexible disk)      28, 39, 77, 79, 93, 97
displayed image factors (fatigue) 113-115
DN-1                58
document preparation     12, 13, 17, 30
dot matrix printer        40, 41, 113

EBCDIC               93, 96
ECMA                94, 102
education and training    133, 134, 135, 137-138
EEC                 53, 86
electronic filing cabinet    14, 17, 82, 85
electronic mail            21, 27, 30, 60, 61, 62, 63-69, 82, 86, 141, 142